Unleashing Your Power

MOVING THROUGH THE TRAUMA OF PARTNER BETRAYAL

Carol Juergensen Sheets ACSW, LCSW, CSAT, CCPS-C, PCC

Christine Turo-Shields ACSW, LCSW, LCAC

SANO PRESS, LLC
CLAREMONT, CA

1st Edition

Cover image by Dumitru, Adobestock.com, standard license. Cover image modified by Chris Bordey. Cover spread, book design, & layout by Chris Bordey.

All images and graphics from Flaticon.com, Pixabay.com, and Unsplash.com in accordance with Creative Commons CC0 except where noted. *Stomach Icon* by Nikita Golubev, Flaticon.com. *Heart Icon* by Freepik, Flaticon.com. Adobestock.com images in use with standard license. Shutterstock.com images in use with standard license. Graphics & Illustrations pp. 20-21, 26-27, 65, & 66 by Chris Bordey. *Ammanda* font commercial license obtained from Creativefabrica.com. *Lucy Rounded* font desktop license with commercial use obtained from Creativemarket.com. All other fonts in use with commercial license from Ultimatefontdownload.com, Fontesk.com, and system fonts. Sano Press feather trademark Sano Press, LLC.

ISBN-13: 978-1-7339222-7-2

ISBN-10: 173392227X

Table of Contents

- Identify the five primary emotions (anger, sadness, happiness, fear and loneliness) to reduce feeling flooded and overwhelmed by a myriad of feelings
- Process feelings in a healthy way and mobilize the needed strength and energy to direct your life
- Assert and communicate your feelings and needs
- Utilize re-parenting skills to maximize your own potential
- Develop and embrace your own self-identity and uniqueness as a woman
- Enhance character strengths that empower you to create the life you envision
- Lessen the impact and control that depression and anxiety may have in your life
- Decrease codependency while increasing self-care
- Increase the ability to meet your own personal needs
- Develop a new sense of self and a vision for the future
- Find your own sense of posttraumatic growth

These exercises were created to do individually by yourself, in conjunction with a "partner sensitive" clinician or coach who can support you through the work, or with a partner sensitive group that focuses on partner betrayal.

Phase One

EXERCISES THAT PROMOTE SAFETY AND STABILIZATION

As a Partner,
I am

As a Partner,
I am not

As a
Recovering Partner,
I want to be

What is a Woman? Exercise

This exercise is to illustrate that you are so much more than what happened to you. We would now like you to identify how you felt about yourself **before** your discovery. There may have been issues in your life that were causing you stress, but hopefully these stressors did not impede on your ability to know your strengths. Remember back to what that was like and pick words that describe the essence of who you were and who you still are. It means you will have to sit quietly and reflect on how you were prior to the trauma. Think about yourself as a young woman, before marriage, before kids, before that first, second or third job. Pick words that describe you **prior** to the betrayal.

- Think about the positive and negative personality strengths that described you before the betrayal.
- Personalize the exercise by asking yourself what words you would use to describe yourself.
- If your list is primarily negative, think about any words that would describe your best friend, sister, or co-workers. Sometimes when you think of the strengths of a friend, you recognize those strengths in yourself.
- Add as many words as you can think of, and don't second-guess yourself!

As you read through the list, circle the words that describe you prior to the betrayal.

giving foolish
PRACTICAL
AWESOME
ARROGANT wise narcissistic Purposeful
SUPPORTIVE fussy Spiritual
ENGAGING HARSH independent
ANGRY OPEN STRONG
PLAYFUL
Whiny
devoted AUTHENTIC RUDE Inspiring
CARING RESILIENT PERSISTENT CLINGY
CONSISTENT needy ANXIOUS
JEALOUS
STUBBORN dependable lonely
GRUMPY Generous
ineffective
empathetic cruel
Brilliant MEAN
Encouraging Faithful
Passionate bitter OVER-WHELMED sexual
LOVING
hopeful pathetic boring
CRITICAL unhappy miserable
HYPERSENSITIVE moody Trust-worthy
weak

Joyful
HOSTILE
DILIGENT
ISOLATED
friendly CHAOTIC CREATIVE
depressed impatient passive
Accepting ENTHUSIASTIC
Compassionate insecure
EMPOWERED polite Intelligent
NURTURING GUARDED
IMPULSIVE DUTIFUL
Judgmental envious
CONNECTED narrow-minded
dependent
humorous
CONTROLLING
asexual greedy COWARDLY
COMPETITIVE depleted
intuitive
Bitchy suspicious
SELFISH EMOTIONAL
TIRED
POWERFUL
thankful
UNDER-STANDING

ADD AT LEAST 10 MORE ADJECTIVES:

If you find that you have primarily circled negative words, we ask that you review the list and pick out at least three to five additional words that describe your strengths. Circle the positive words, even if your critical voice tells you that you do not deserve to "claim" them. We all have positive qualities, so it is important to recognize and own them. It is time to change these distortions and this exercise helps you to examine your thoughts and begin to change them.

- Think about the positive and negative personality strengths that describe women.
- Personalize the exercise by asking yourself what words you would use to describe yourself.
- Add to the list any adjectives that would describe your mother, sister, best friend, mentor, teacher, etc.
- If your list is primarily negative, think about a woman who you admire and add positive words that describe her.
- Add as many words as you can think of, have fun with it and don't second-guess yourself!

As you read through the following list, circle those words that apply to your personality and character traits.

We also ask that you add at least ten other adjectives to your list.

After you have circled the adjectives that describe yourself and have added at least ten additional adjectives, complete the following statements by using those adjectives. Limit your choice of adjectives to only one per statement. Women are renowned for fragmenting or fracturing themselves—this exercise is meant to focus you on your identity and to remember who you were before betrayal.

As a woman,
I am

As a woman,
I am not

CREATE A GOAL STATEMENT

Now look at the differences between the "As a partner" statements and "As a woman" statements and ask yourself if you are ready to move into a more stabilized place where you can refocus on you and own who you are separate from what happened to you. Read the "As a woman" statements out loud to see how they resonate with you. The final statement, "As a woman, I want to be ..." now becomes your vision of yourself as you continue your path of personal transformation. It will help to restore your sense of safety and stabilization because it restores YOU.

To further anchor this new sense of identity, post this statement in highly visible places. You may also find that creating a collage or vision board will reinforce this self-discovery. *In Chapter 2 you will learn how to create a vision board to begin to see yourself as moving out of this trauma.

Don't underestimate the power of your third statement, which is really an affirmation of who you want to be. Retraining the brain to recognize your strengths is a powerful tool to evoking change and personal transformation. If you find yourself really having difficulty, you might add the words "in the process of," which infers that you are a work in progress!

- "As a woman, I want to be strong," becomes...
    - As a woman, I am in the process of gaining strength.

or

- "As a woman, I want to be assertive," becomes...
    - As a woman, I am in the process of being assertive.

After partner betrayal, partners are often unclear about what they want in their lives. Additionally, you may be unsure as to what goals to work on. The final statement in the "What Is a Woman?" activity allows you to own what you want to work toward on your own personal journey!

The following examples illustrate this point:

- As a woman, I am weak and dependent.
- As a woman, I am not powerful.
- As a woman, I want to be strong.

This becomes not only your anchor—your vision—but a goal statement that you will explore throughout this workbook. By raising this into your conscious awareness, you can actively pursue creating the life you desire and deserve. It will help to move you to that third phase of restoration which automatically places you into a state of posttraumatic growth.

You may not be consciously aware of this, but you are articulating a goal of assertiveness. Ask yourself, "What have I learned about myself since the betrayal and what additional skills am I learning by being strong?" Most likely, being strong means being clear and direct about your needs and wants, so you will want to work on developing this skill as you navigate this workbook.

The aforementioned anchor will guide you throughout this workbook but, more importantly, throughout your life. Your theme will be reiterated throughout your personal journey.

> *Therapeutically, this workbook provides and creates many opportunities for you to push beyond what you believe are your limitations or weaknesses. It helps you push beyond partner betrayal.*

The next step is to visualize what you want to become and how you want to shift at this time in your life.

RETRAIN YOUR BRAIN BY OWNING YOUR POWER

The shock of sexual betrayal has temporarily caused your brain to go into overdrive. As you know, the amygdala went into fight, flight or freeze mode to protect you. Your emotional center, the anterior cingulate which regulates your emotions, went into distress and has likely flooded you with feelings. You felt a deep sense of rejection that caused your parasympathetic nervous system to shut down. Messages were sent to the prefrontal cortex in such a hyper-aroused state that your executive functioning also shut down making it difficult to think and make decisions. You most likely had trouble participating in daily routines like eating, sleeping and daily hygiene. Luckily, as things began to calm down and you were able to make better sense of what happened to you, your brain was able to get back online. As you continue this journey of self-discovery, you will have a better sense of who you are and what you want in life. You will have more confidence and a stronger sense of self.

Retraining your brain to see your positive attributes takes practice. It can be an exciting process to create your self-identity to be the woman you were meant to be. Imagine that you could paint a canvas of who you wanted to be. As a painter, you have the capability to use an entire color palette and various textures to enhance your strengths and portray yourself as a strong, powerful woman.

Well, the truth of the matter is that you already are strong and creative; you are already intelligent and strategic. Perhaps you are simply lacking the reminders that will retrain the brain to have belief in yourself.

> *This journey requires that you retrain your brain to recognize how you have mobilized great strengths from this trauma. To do this requires that you retrain your self-concept by retraining your brain.*

USE YOUR UNCONSCIOUS

The unconscious is a very powerful tool and when it repeatedly experiences a visual image, it goes into overdrive to make that vision a reality. Since partner betrayal, you have had to endure all of those frightening discoveries that put unhealthy thoughts and images into your head. After you experience trauma, it has a tendency to keep you stuck in the moment of discovery and will keep you locked in a place that keeps you fearful of going forward. You will have trouble believing in yourself, believing that the relationship can ever be real again, and believing that you will ever have the future you deserve, with or without the addict. Retraining your brain will automatically change both your unconscious and subconscious to find opportunities to support you because you have recognized the essence of your power.

You truly are the creator of your life and you can create the life you deserve. To make the unconscious-conscious requires constant input of recognizing and acknowledging the strength within.

On the next page is an exercise to begin the process and remind you of your brilliance!

THE NAME GAME

Use the letters of your name to create a visual of your strengths on a piece of paper or on the computer. If you struggle with identifying positive words, choose some listed from the "What Is a Woman?" exercise that you previously completed. We have provided two examples for you.

As a woman, I am, or as I woman, I want to be:

This is **Carol's** Visual Reminder.

C–Connected

H–HOPEFUL

R–RESILIENT

I—Intelligent

S—Spiritual

T–Thankful

I-Interdependent

N–Nurturing

E–Encouraging

This is **Christine's** Visual Aid.

Add artwork to your name, enlarge the font, and make it an expression of your affirmation. Get creative and place it somewhere where you will see it often to remind you of your personal greatness.

CHAPTER 2

Develop Your Vision

RESOURCING AND GROUNDING THROUGH THE BETRAYAL

What Do You Need to Self-Actualize?

Most women are scheduled so tightly, they have very little time to listen to their intuition, a practice which can guide them into deep transformation. This is greatly exacerbated by the trauma that you have experienced. You not only are on overdrive, but your prefrontal cortex has been assaulted and it is as if you no longer have the capacity to think clearly.

To complicate things further, you were put into a stress response state which took away from this mission and left you scrambling to understand how partner betrayal could have occurred. You spent most of your waking moments thinking about HIM and the betrayal, leaving you exhausted and depleted. To undo the damage that has been done and to tap into your purpose—your vision—you must find time daily to contemplate, meditate, reflect and breathe.

It is time to focus on your self-actualization. It is a way to move closer towards restoration so that you can recalibrate and find the woman that you were meant to be!

Perhaps you already have a clear idea of the transformations you would like to see in your life, or maybe you are not sure what direction you should move. Either way, spend a few moments in quiet reflection to allow your vision of yourself to surface. After centering yourself, spend some time writing about your thoughts. The act of writing it down is the first step in making your visions a reality.

After completing this exercise, one woman became aware that her life was off balance as she juggled her hectic schedule and roles as a mother, business owner and spouse. Prior to the exercise, she thought she needed to be more efficient in her life. What she learned from the exercise was that she needed more balance to better care for herself. She was amazed at what her intuition told her when she slowed down enough to listen to what was within.

Had sex addiction not entered your life, what direction or path were you taking to actualize your potential and to be all that you could be?

If this had not happened to you, what would your vision be for yourself and your life?

Now that this has happened to you, how might you use it to create a new vision?

CREATING MORE SAFETY IN YOUR LIFE

Carving some time out of your schedule daily for meditating, contemplating, and reflecting will help you be more successful with this exercise and with progressing toward your vision. We have a meditation later in the book that can help build your sense of identity and strength. Meditation is instrumental in calming down the trauma that has occurred because of the betrayal; it can be an excellent way to slow down your racing thoughts. It is an excellent tool in grounding and resourcing.

To develop this habit, consider the following:

- What time of day or night works best for you to sit quietly for five to ten minutes in deep thought?
- What place can you designate as your quiet place or sacred spot to meditate?
- What supports can you utilize to give yourself uninterrupted time?

CREATE A VISION BOARD TO REMIND YOURSELF THAT YOU ARE MORE THAN "WHAT HAPPENED TO YOU"

YOU HAVE THE POWER TO CREATE A NEW EXPERIENCE

Become the architect of your life! Beginning with the positive words you identified in the "What is a Woman?" exercise, cut out pictures, symbols, and words that reflect and depict those adjectives. Imagine that you could design your life visually by creating a collage that embraces the woman you are and/or the woman you want to be in the future. This may seem difficult considering the betrayal. Your future may feel like it has been contaminated, but you have the power to change that!

Your restoration depends on being able to create a new vision that centers on you and what you would like to see for your own mental health and future. Think about the many dreams and goals you have for your life and find pictures that reflect the life that you want for yourself.

Playfully have fun with this project and imagine that what you create on the paper or poster board could become your reality—because it can!

A vision board is a collection of pictures and symbols that represent what you want in your life. It is like a collage or map of how you envision your destiny.

What would you put on your vision board? What goals, aspirations and dreams do you have? Would you like to change jobs or have better relationships with your kids? Do you hope to forgive your partner someday, improve your health, lose some weight, become more assertive and direct, increase your confidence, let go of your anger or forgive the church that blamed you for his poor choices?

In a very visual sense, the vision board depicts what you want to attract in your life. Begin by finding pictures of healthy relationships, strong and confident women, activities that promote fitness, etc.

This exercise is enlightening as it shows you the possibilities for your life ahead—how it is going to be different with your new focus and new direction. When you have been traumatized it can be difficult to believe that you could ever see the possibilities for the future. We know that trauma stops you from envisioning your future. This exercise is a measurable tool to slowly begin the process of designing your new life after betrayal. As you view your pictures, you have the understandable limiting belief that says, "I will never be able to smile again, or "I will never be able to achieve family cohesiveness in my future" or I will never be able to feel secure or safe again." This visual representation of what you want becomes the vehicle for designing your own life. Don't underestimate the power of your vision!

Grab an assortment of magazines, get out your scissors and glue or tape, and create that vision board! We have encouraged you to use the space in the book for starters, however you may find it more beneficial to use a big poster board. When you're done, place it in a spot where you can regularly see it. Then step back and watch it work its magic!

You may ask how a piece of your artwork could make a real impact on your life. The vision board provides an opportunity for you to retrain the brain and envision a difference in your life. It reminds you of the possibilities. It helps to create a life that is no longer focused on betrayal, but instead focuses on who YOU are and what you want for your future!

Paste your vision board here!

STRENGTHENING YOUR SELF-ESTEEM

As you continue your journey, consider whether you view yourself as someone who has high self-esteem or low self-esteem. We know that your self-esteem was greatly impacted by the betrayal and the trauma. However, you don't have to be defined by it. All spiritual walks maintain that your suffering can lead to great transformation, which results in self-actualization, which creates purpose and vision. You would NEVER have asked for this trauma, but it can help you to grow and learn from it. The exercises in this workbook can help increase self-esteem no matter where you see yourself right now. If you historically have had low self-esteem, you may need to spend some significant time in this chapter.

> *All spiritual walks maintain that your suffering can lead to great transformation, which results in self-actualization, which creates purpose and vision.*

For some women who have been traumatized, low self-esteem may have originated in childhood. It may be a result of how you were raised and invalidated as a child. Perhaps you lived with an alcoholic parent, watched your parents go through a horrible divorce, or were molested as a child. You may have experienced posttraumatic stress disorder, feeling a pervasive sense of insecurity about your environment and yourself.

This, coupled with your spouse living a secret life that you knew nothing about, created a sense that you could not trust the person you loved most and the life you thought the two of you had created together. Everything you knew was a lie, leaving you wondering why God would have allowed this to happen to you. Your existential sense of the world has left you wondering what you can count on and how can you depend on anything or anyone again. No wonder you don't feel safe!

You are learning in this book that you can't change your past ... but you can choose to build on your strengths and count on you! And as you do, you will come to the realization that the world did NOT do this to you; instead the world allowed for your husband to participate in an activity that became compulsive. Spiritual teachings allow people to have self-determination. This meant that your husband became vulnerable to an addiction that took him down and robbed you of your sense of self, safety and intuition. The addiction did that, not the world!

The good news is that you are rebuilding your self-esteem, and that you, as an adult, can heal from the wrongs that happened to you in your past. Although it takes work, discipline and a positive belief that you are worth it to increase self-esteem, it IS **achievable!**

BE GENTLE WITH YOURSELF

The number one statement women make when their self-esteem has been assaulted is, "I am not good enough."

Let's look at the earliest memories that may have contributed to childhood low self-worth. (If your childhood was solid and healthy you can skip this part). However, we encourage you to list some negative messages you may have received even if you had a positive childhood.

Did this occur first in your childhood? Did you receive or experience a lot of negative messages as a child? This may have left you feeling disempowered and "less than." Perhaps your parents were discouraging or told you that you could not accomplish certain things in your life. Just as insidious, one or both of them may not have been emotionally available to you. Often, parents were not around to validate you or identify your strengths. This typically happened when a parent was an alcoholic or other type of abuser: a workaholic, a betrayer or narcissist, to name a few. It can be difficult as a child to build positive self-esteem in the face of that reality.

Spend some time on the next few pages writing about the messages you received as a child and how this robbed you of your sense of self.

How did low self-esteem first occur in your childhood?

What negative messages did you receive as child?

How were your parents discouraging?

How were your parents unavailable?

As a partner moving toward posttraumatic growth, you need to identify your strengths and remind yourself of your own potential. This may look like the following:

- Remind yourself daily of your own internal strengths. This means looking in the mirror and telling yourself that you are confident, capable, kind-hearted, smart, intuitive and loving.
- Make gentle statements that encourage you to set boundaries, assert yourself or gently push you towards taking the next step.
- Practice making statements to yourself that an ideal parent would have told you as you were growing up.

Here are some examples of what that may sound like:

- "I know that you don't want to enforce the boundaries, but you deserve to have safety. And if he won't or can't honor what you need, you are going to have to stand strong and enforce them yourself!"
- "I know you don't feel like you can ask for the promotion, but truly you are ready for this assignment and would do an excellent job performing your new work duties."
- "I know you're afraid to date since your nasty divorce, but you have so much to offer another person and need to practice having fun with other men so that you can begin to trust again."

Self-compassion is the practice of talking to yourself as an ideal parent or a dear friend. It reminds you to be kinder and gentler to yourself and affirms that you have the courage to take the risks necessary to have the experiences you deserve. Having experienced sexual betrayal means that you need to double down on using nurturing self-talk and make it a point to recognize any stressor and advocate for YOU. There are many losses that erode our self-esteem: losses such as the inability to go to college, divorce, fractured relationships, chronic health conditions or the death of a child.

In these types of situations, it is important to be your own best cheerleader. This might look like the following:

- You have just found out about another acting out scenario that occurred in your spouse's history. You know that this does not necessarily mean that he is acting out now, but it requires that you reorient to the here and now and readjust accordingly. You tell yourself that you are safe right now and take some deep breaths and move through the trigger.

- You are on your way home from work and you get a speeding ticket. Instead of telling yourself you're stupid, unobservant and a screw-up, you tell yourself that this was a good life lesson to remember to slow down and that perhaps this saved you from an accident had you continued to speed.

- Your husband asks you for a divorce. You feel rejected, sad, and worthless. You ask yourself, what did you do to cause his rejection? You begin to question why you were not worthy of his love.

  You then reorient and remind yourself that his addiction had nothing to do with you. He is very sick right now and nothing can break the chains of his self-absorbed illness. The addiction has robbed him of his good judgement and if he does not want you, then it IS best that he let you go so that you can find the love you deserve.

  You may not be there yet but eventually you will be reminding yourself that you can grow from this situation and discover why you ultimately will be better off single. You might tell yourself that this will give you a chance to learn more about yourself, spend more time with the kids, and explore what you really want in life. If he is not going to repair the situation, you will need to continue to look within and begin to look for others to help you heal.

It may sound unrealistic, but your thoughts and your self-talk "work if you work them." The important thing is to practice the skills regularly so that they become a natural part of your coping mechanisms and prompt you to feel good about yourself no matter the circumstance. Be your own cheerleader...your self-esteem will thank you!

Your thoughts and your self-talk "work if you work them." The important thing is to practice the skills regularly so that they become a natural part of your coping mechanisms and prompt you to feel good about yourself no matter what the circumstance.

The following exercises will help you further enhance your self-identity, increase your self-esteem and allow you to process core issues or improve your body image.

CHAPTER 3

Increase Your Resilience

FINDING YOUR STRENGTH AMIDST THE CRISIS

Develop the Art of Personal Resiliency

When partners are trying to find safety and to stabilize, it is not unusual for them to get stuck or mired by their betrayal, continually replaying the negative situations or feelings that happened to them. In trying to fit the pieces together, they replay the details and facts over and over, which is both depleting and exhausting, making the future seem less hopeful. If this sounds like you, it is time to take back your power and look for your personal resiliency. Remember that resiliency is the goal of Phase 3-Restoration. Restoration or Posttraumatic growth is a process and it starts in Phase I, so it requires that you own your thoughts and your story. This means that you must not take on the negative beliefs that can accompany betrayal.

It can be challenging to see that the struggles of the past truly allow for the gifts of today. Partners can be resistive to this because they do not in any way want to legitimize what has been done to them. But you are not only a survivor, you are a thriver! You just need to retrieve your energy and find yourself again. Don't cheat yourself out of acknowledging your strengths and coping skills. It is important for partners to acknowledge that the obstacles they have faced in the past have positively contributed to the women they are today.

You will find a purpose as a result of this betrayal and chaos. Take Oprah for example; as she celebrated the opening of her leadership school for girls in South Africa, she was able to recognize that the vision for this school was a culmination of all her life experiences, including that of being sexually abused, raped and growing up in poverty.

You will find a purpose as a result of this betrayal and chaos.

One of the most important skills a woman can master is resiliency. When you develop resilience, you will be able to see some powerful things that have come out of this horrible ordeal.

Resilience is the capacity to recover from difficulties or the ability to see the positive in any situation. We must be able to see that we are the sum of all our life experiences: good and bad, joyful and sorrowful—that we have attained a certain wisdom from all of these circumstances.

Part of your self-exploration will be learning new skills that will teach you about your own inner strength that resulted from partner betrayal. Take some time to think about how your life circumstances have made you the woman you are today.

Looking back allows you to acknowledge and embrace your history, or as we prefer to call it, your "her-story." What difficulties have you had in your life? What obstacles have you faced? What demons have you encountered? What is your her-story?

For this next exercise, we have provided a series of questions to answer prior to writing your her-story. They are designed to help you identify your resiliency.

What are the defining moments in my life?

What did these life experiences teach me about who I am?

How have I grown stronger as a result of these significant life events?

How have I been shaped or imprinted by my childhood?

What are the life lessons that have carried me into my adulthood?

What did I learn about myself through those experiences?

How did this betrayal make me stronger?

What have I learned about my coping skills because of it?

How might I want to help others because of my trauma?

Be sure to include the lessons that you have learned as well as the actual life events. As a result of writing her "her-story," one woman learned that her molestation as a child had kept her feeling unsafe, invisible and not worthy. She had lived her whole life like that and never felt like she had a voice. When the multiple betrayals happened to her, it reinforced her sense of invisibility. After she wrote her "her-story," she decided to take back her power. She used her goal "What is a Woman?" statement which was "As a Woman, I want to be empowered" and she thought about what she would need to feel empowered. She recognized that she needed boundaries with consequences to keep her safe. She realized that she did have a voice but, in the past, she had been too scared to use it. She wrote out some assertiveness statements that were clear and direct and she practiced them diligently in the mirror. When she was ready, she went to an attorney, set up her divorce and then went home and insisted on meeting with her husband to share the boundaries. She told him she was tired of his addiction, had filed for a divorce and insisted that he go to a treatment facility for sex addiction. She explained that this would be the first of many requests that she would make of him and if he did not cooperate, she would seek divorce. She told him she would no longer live like this!

Another woman did her "her-story" and realized that as a result of growing up with a rage-aholic mother, she had actually gained a Teflon coating that allowed her to reject the hostility and projections of her husband after discovery. She knew his acting out was not about her, and she fiercely opposed his attempts to blame her for his addiction. When she did this exercise, she was able to embrace the gift of Teflon received from her mother rather than focus on the pain inflicted by her mother.

WRITE YOUR HISTORY—YOUR "HER-STORY"

Take as much time as you need to write your life "her-story." You may find that the words flow easily on paper, or you may need to break it into segments of your life (such as childhood, adolescence, young adulthood, middle age, and your older adult years).

MY PERSONAL HER-STORY

MY PERSONAL HER-STORY (cont.)

MY PERSONAL HER-STORY (cont.)

CHAPTER 4

Feeling Identification

STOP THE FLOODING OF FEELINGS BY PICKING THE PRIMARY FEELING

Your Primary Feeling Can Motivate You

Do you feel stuck in betrayal? Are you having difficulty detaching from the trauma and moving on? It may be that you have not worked through the feelings of betrayal. They may have immobilized you and kept you tethered to him and the pain. You will have many opportunities to work through your grief and mourning in Phase 2, but first you must become astute at feeling your primary feeling.

Let's do a check-in and assess your feelings.

- Have you given yourself enough time to be angry or grieve the losses this has caused?
- Are there areas of your life that stay the same despite your desire to change?
- Do you wonder why you just can't get over the hurdles and make your life different?

Your emotions may be what are holding you back from becoming the woman you really want to be. To identify your feelings, it is helpful to reduce the emotions to five basic feelings:

- Anger
- Sadness
- Happiness
- Fear
- Loneliness

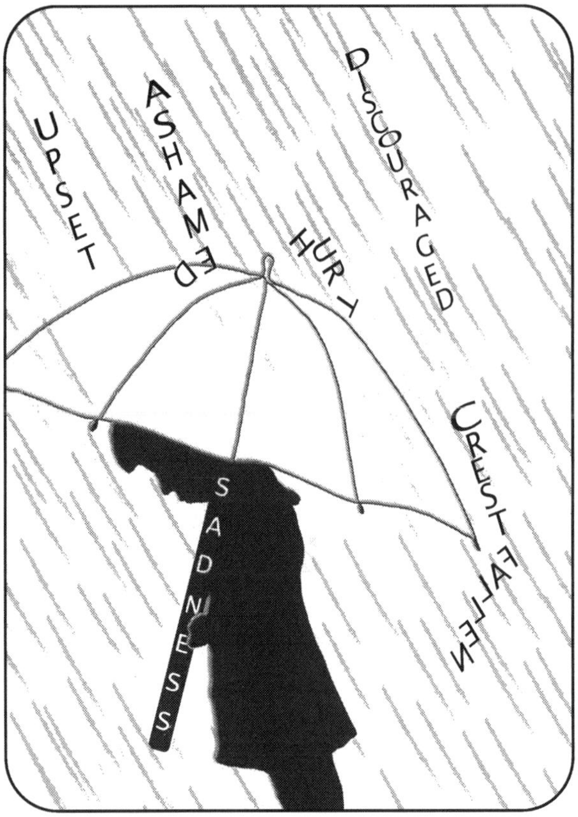
UPSET
ASHAMED
DISCOURAGED
HURT
CRESTFALLEN
SADNESS

EXCITED
EXUBERANT
GOOD
JOYFUL
SERENE
ENTHUSED
HAPPINESS

WORRIED
SCARED
FEARFUL
ANXIOUS
UNSURE
FEAR

DIFFERENT
ALONE
LESS THAN
REJECTED
ISOLATED

You may prefer to identify your feelings with the following kid-friendly words: Since the first three rhyme, it is easy to remember the "famous five feelings":

- Mad
- Sad
- Glad
- Afraid
- Lonely

All emotions can be condensed down to any of these "famous five feelings." The difficult task is to determine which feeling is predominant at the time. You may be aware that you feel several feelings at one time. Oftentimes, the feeling most uncomfortable for you is the one you avoid. Women typically feel and express sadness when their main feeling is really anger. Alternatively, men typically report anger when the uncomfortable feeling is generally fear or sadness.

Where do you feel personally stuck? Take a few moments and think of which part of the betrayal seems the most problematic?

Does it affect your sense of safety? If so, how does that make you feel?

Does it make you feel unworthy? What is the primary feeling that links up to "unworthiness"?

Has it shattered your sense of the world? What feeling does that evoke in you?

Which feeling is the most overwhelming as you think of the betrayal?

The three feelings that typically stop women from moving through their issues are anger, fear and sadness. It is imperative that you identify what feeling is really immobilizing you. Doing this will motivate you to take care of yourself differently.

Here are some examples:

- A woman is betrayed when her husband has multiple affairs. She feels sad and depressed about his chronic cheating and is left feeling immobilized because she is in agony about having to change her whole life; yet when she sits with the feelings, she realizes she is angry because her entire life is going to have to change and she can't begin to decide what is in her best interest. She KNOWS that she will never be able to trust him.

  This woman needed to feel anger instead of sadness. It gave her the adrenaline she needed to start working on how she was going to recover from the betrayal. Staying stuck in the sadness left her feeling lethargic. It kept her in the victim role.

  When she got in touch with her anger, she began to focus on herself and she set aside time specifically to look at what she needed if she was going to become a single mother. She used the anger to energize her into taking better care of herself, which included activities such as playing tennis and attending church more regularly.

- A woman has lost her house because of her husband's financial irresponsibility. He was as addicted to compulsive spending as he was to acting out. At 54 years old, she had worked her whole life to have a home, a family and financial security, and now she realized her whole life was a lie. As she sat with her feelings, she found that fear was her primary feeling. She was worried that she would be unable to recoup from the financial devastation and understood that it would alter her family's lifestyle. As she examined her fears, she was able to use techniques to rebuild her confidence and look at her life differently. She decided she would pursue real estate and buy low-income properties. She worked her budget and refinanced her assets, and two years later she has become financially solvent, pursuing a dream that became a reality by default. Identifying her fear helped her to realize she could take charge of her own finances and rebuild her sense of financial stability.

Don't let your feelings confuse you. Identify them and then use them to propel you toward your desired transformation.

What situation have you encountered and felt personally overwhelmed by?

What was the primary feeling and how did it affect your choices?

How could you use this feeling to motivate you to make some needed changes?

Feelings Check-In

We find that partners not only have the burden of trying to figure out what happened to them, but also the burden of how to prevent further traumatic events. This hypervigilance about keeping themselves safe is exhausting and interferes with the normal "mental health hygiene" of checking in with one's feelings.

Traditionally, women are so busy and so used to multitasking most of their waking day that they are left fragmented and they forget to check in with their own needs and wants. This, coupled with partner betrayal, requires a "structured approach" to putting themselves first.

The following exercises allow you to assess how you feel and what you want, which helps to direct your energies towards what is best for you in your daily living.

THE DAILY FEELINGS CHECK-IN FORMAT

The following format allows you to take some quiet time and assess what you want for the day. This simple tool empowers you to put yourself on the front burner and decide how you want to live your day and what direction you want to take for the day. It is a simple exercise of self-empowerment. Our belief is that when you tune in to what you need, you will be more likely to have enough energy for both yourself and others. Yet most busy women require a regular time for check-ins. Once they have established the structure and time for this process, they will intermittently use it when they need to assess a problem or dilemma in their day.

The daily "Feelings Check-In" allows you to:

- Be in the moment
- Pay attention to what is going on inside of you
- Nurture yourself

- Let go of all things of which you had no control. Although you are trying to ascertain what you might have control over keeping yourself safe, it can be freeing to let go of the need to manage all of his whereabouts and activities. Now that you know what he did, he will never be able to deceive you fully again!

The "Feelings Check-in" is the vehicle that allows you this opportunity. It is important for you to check in with your feelings and expectations daily and to encourage yourself to be accountable for your life.

The format is quite simple and is as follows on the next page...

Feelings Check-In

RIGHT HERE & NOW, I FEEL *(CIRCLE ONE)*:

MAD *SAD* *GLAD* *AFRAID* *LONELY*

THE REASON I FEEL THAT WAY IS BECAUSE:

WHAT DO I NEED TO DO TO CREATE MORE EMOTIONAL SAFETY?

WHAT DO I NEED TO DO TO SET STRONGER BOUNDARIES?

I NEED TO REMIND MYSELF THAT MY LIFE IS NOT ALL BAD.
DESPITE THE ORDEAL, WHAT I APPRECIATE IN MY LIFE RIGHT NOW IS:

HOW CAN I APPROACH THE DAY TO FEEL MORE EMPOWERED?

WHAT MIGHT I NEED TO LET GO OF TO BE MORE FULLY PRESENT?

AS A RECOVERING PARTNER, I NEED TO RELINQUISH CONTROL AND GIVE UP THE FOLLOWING BEHAVIOR TO SAVE MORE SPACE FOR ME:

THE 24-HOUR REFLECTION FORMAT

Pick one primary feeling to list in your check-in, even if you're experiencing all five feelings! Women are already so fragmented and take so little time to focus their attention on one, and only one, issue or feeling. This exercise provides an opportunity to do so. If you are like most partners, you are typically flooded by a host of feelings. It is important to remind yourself that emotions fall into one of the five feeling categories.

Identifying your primary feeling allows you to focus on one single emotion. When you are flooded with emotions, it's easier to become immobilized or paralyzed by them.

The details of the betrayal may paint the picture and set the stage, but they are not the essence of healing and transformation. You and your feelings create the change!

Partner betrayal has already left you so fragmented. It can take much effort for you to feel safe and as a result, it can deplete you from being able to take time to focus your attention on one issue or feeling that is predominant in your life. The details of the betrayal may paint the picture and set the stage, but they are not the essence of healing and transformation. You and your feelings are!

Writing out your feelings can help ground you in the "here and now," as well as gently remind you of your desire to transform into the woman you want to become, which leads to restoration. It can be helpful to reflect on your past twenty-four hours to better focus on the changes you want to make in your next twenty-four hours. Here is another format you can use to keep your awareness in the present.

24-Hour Reflection

RIGHT HERE & NOW, I FEEL *(CIRCLE ONE)*:

MAD *SAD* *GLAD* *AFRAID* *LONELY*

BRIEF DESCRIPTION OF THE PAST 24 HOURS:

ONE THING THAT I WILL FOCUS ON TODAY TO IMPROVE MY SENSE OF SELF:

ONE THING THAT I AM WILLING TO LET GO OF TODAY THAT IS NOT WITHIN MY CONTROL:

EXAMPLE OF A "24-HOUR REFLECTION"

24-Hour Reflection

RIGHT HERE & NOW, I FEEL (*CIRCLE ONE*):

MAD (circled) *SAD* *GLAD* *AFRAID* *LONELY*

I feel angry because I am reading betrayal literature and listening to podcasts while my husband is off playing golf with his buddies.

BRIEF DESCRIPTION OF THE PAST 24 HOURS:

I have been really tired, as I have stayed up late with the baby and have done nothing for myself.

ONE THING THAT I WILL FOCUS ON TODAY TO IMPROVE MY SENSE OF SELF:

I will call Jill and ask if she will come over so that I can run some errands and go to the gym for some exercise.

ONE THING THAT I AM WILLING TO LET GO OF TODAY THAT IS NOT WITHIN MY CONTROL:

I will let go of my resentment toward my husband for meeting his needs and refocus on taking better care of mine. I will join that partner betrayal support group because my therapist recommends it. I keep resisting it because I don't have enough time. But I will put myself first and make the time to create the support I deserve!

FEELINGS COLOR CALENDAR

We know that feelings are neither good nor bad, they just are. Colors also are neither good nor bad, they just are...so add a little color to your feelings.

Assign colors to your feelings. One woman chose:

- anger–red
- sad–blue
- happy–yellow
- afraid/anxious–green
- lonely–purple

Now it's your turn. You may easily have colors in mind that represent your feelings. If not, close your eyes and think of a situation that caused you to feel each of the feelings below. Allow a color to come to mind and write it down. Remember there is no right or wrong color assignment.

- anger ______________________________
- sad ______________________________
- happy ______________________________
- afraid/anxious ________________________
- lonely ______________________________

Once you have your feeling colors identified, then begin to log your feelings color calendar daily. You may choose to use a paper calendar or create one on your computer. Each day, color the block on a calendar to represent your primary feeling for the day. You may find it is one solid color, or you may split the block to represent the shifts that occur. For instance, you may have felt happy (yellow) in the morning, but sad (blue) throughout the rest of the day.

The color calendar provides a quick visual to examine how you are feeling, which allows you to honor your feelings as well as choose what you can do to meet your needs to work through the anger, sadness, fear or loneliness that you may be feeling.

When you link the color to the feeling, you can learn to manage your emotions in lots of different ways. You can practice learning how to turn up or turn down your feelings so that you can navigate through them more effectively. Despite what has been done to you, you too, have the capability of affecting change. Altering a color in the mind creates unconscious and subconscious change that will continue to train your brain to be less traumatized.This technique is often used in hypnosis. Visualizing turning down the anxiety can actually reduce the anxiety in your day.

Let's say that you are sad about your anniversary because your anniversary no longer represents your marital vows or your special connection. It is a tough day for you and you feel overwhelmed by your sadness. Imagine, if you will, that you can breathe in the color that your sadness represents. As you breathe, you can visualize the blue becoming lighter or softer. Ask yourself what might contribute to feeling less sad. Maybe it would be recognizing that your husband is in recovery. Perhaps it is thinking of your incredible kids who were born out of this union. Or possibly you are recognizing how much better you are feeling despite the original trauma you may simultaneously be feeling. Many women feel it helpful to tell their husbands that they are having a blue day or a green day. Believe it or not, many husbands mirror the association and share with their wives that they too, are having blue or green days. Just remember that your brain is a powerful tool and imagery is an effective way of both changing your thoughts and feelings and feeling more comfortable with them.

MANAGING YOUR BETRAYAL TRIGGERS

Triggers are either external or internal. They may occur because there has been something that has occurred that reminded you of the contamination that occurred the last time you had the memory of having been together and that contamination has ruined all the previous times that you thought were special between you. Or maybe it is a trigger because you pass a hotel that he had cheated in, or a massage parlor where he acted out. You know why you are having the trigger and it frustrates you that it seems like your whole life has been discredited.

Sometimes a trigger can occur out of the blue. You have no understanding as to why it has happened, but it leaves you feeling vulnerable, helpless, scared, attacked, out of control and confused. You are wanting to make sense of your life, but things are happening to you that don't add up and the worst thing about it is that it makes you feel "crazy." Triggers can be initiated by the unconscious and it might be a smell, a taste, a touch, an image or a sound that activates it and permeates your sense of safety.

Triggers feel unmanageable and are like daggers to your heart. They have attached to the past betrayal, past traumas and the current stressors in your life. If your spouse is inconsistent in his promises or does something that heightens the behaviors that were reminiscent of his addiction, it will catapult you into fear and frenzy. Triggers hijack your brain, emotions and spirit and cause you to wonder if you will ever get better.

When you are seeking safety, you must find ways to turn down the intensity and the frequency to better cope with a signal that is linked to the past.

There are primarily 3 ways to cope with triggers. The first is to practice mindfulness both to reduce the frequency and intensity of the trigger and to work towards preventing its presence.

The second is to remind yourself that a trigger is about the past and not the present. Telling yourself that you are safe in the here and now and that nothing bad is happening to you right now is a positive way to calm your fears, slow down your brain, ground and resource you in the present. Training your brain to remain in the "here and now" will increase emotional regulation.

The third way to manage triggers is to create a network of safe people whom you can share your emotions. A trauma therapist or partner sensitive counselor or coach will work with you to practice the tools to calm the triggers.

Sometimes your husband will be able to help you with your triggers. In the workbook *Help. Her. Heal.* written by Carol, there is a step by step formula that Dorit Reichental and Janice Caudill created to help couples work through the triggers.

Here is the summary of the valuable work that they offered.

Dorit Reichental and Janice Caudill have come up with a trigger busters protocol for your spouse which can help you and your spouse to work through the triggers together. They basically have broken it down into 4 stages whereby your spouse can initially respond with the following:

TO THE ADDICT

1. Identify what you believe that you are noticing with your partner in the here and now. You then ask "Are you triggered?" You then validate what you are seeing which in most cases is the trigger. "I can see that you are triggered" or, "it makes sense to me that you would be triggered."

2. Help her to stay grounded to the here and now by orienting her to the present. Remind her that she is safe and nothing bad is happening now.

3. De-escalate the experience by saying something nurturing and safe. "I am not doing anything now that would put you in harm's way." Or "That is a bad trigger and happened when I was acting out in the past. I am not acting out now, so remember that you are safe and I am right here."

4. In this step you can sit with her and report what you believe you are seeing that may be indicative that she has managed the trigger. You act as her mirror giving her feedback when it appears that she seems to be co-regulating. You have gone through the trigger busters cycle together!

Dorit and Janice explain that when a trigger occurs the left brain goes offline and a partner's emotions and feelings will go on overload. When this happens the sex addict can help her self-regulate by going through the process together.

The following page contains Dorit's and Janice's Cheat Sheet for what they call Relational CPR for Sexual Addiction and Triggers.

Trigger Busters: Relational CPR

4 STEPS TO SAFETY & CO-REGULATION

Trigger Activation:

- Triggered Partner (TP): left brain goes offline, right brain takes over and TP free falls down the rabbit hole.
- Sex Addict (SA) must reach into the rabbit hole and guide TP back into the Window of Tolerance ASAP
- SA holds all the power to either be the hero who rescues the TP or lets the TP continue free falling down the rabbit hole.

Step 1: Identity the Trigger

1. **Clarification:** Clarify if spouse is triggered.
   "I can see X, Y, Z. Are you triggered?"
2. **Accountability:** DO NOT defend, blame, shame, minimize, invalidate, judge, criticize, debate, stonewall, correct with irrelevant detail, withdraw, escape, or project anger.
3. **Validation:** As soon as SA realizes that spouse is triggered he validates the TP.
   "I can see how scared and unsafe you are, it must remind you of...It makes sense to me that you feel triggered, scared, angry, unsafe etc."

Step 2: Orient to here and Now

- SA gently reminds the IP that she is safe, nothing bad is happening right now because the triggered partner cannot differentiate between past and present.
  "I am not doing anything now to put you at risk or in danger; it's a bad trigger, that happened when I was acting out. I am not acting out now, you are safe and I am right here with you."

Step 3: De-escalation, Safety, & Stabilization Using Trigger Busters

- What does a nurturing/protective SA in recovery need to say and do to help the TP down-regulate?

  As the hijacked brain comes back online, the SA empathically attunes to the partner and states:
  "I can see this was a really bad trigger. You are safe right now.
  I have your back."

- What does the nurturing/protective partner need to say and do to help himself down-regulate in order to be there for the TP?

Step 4: Social Engagement

- What are the somatic, felt sense signs, that the trigger is being defused?

ADDITIONAL RELATIONAL TRIGGER BUSTERS

- Trigger Busting Plan for managing predictable triggers
- Trigger Busting Plan for neutralizing or managing triggers around special events
- Social re-engagement strategies: engaging the 5 senses

It can feel overwhelming to be sidelined by your triggers. There are many ways to have a different relationship with them, but it requires some creativity to shift how they make you feel.

Imagine identifying three common triggers that can take you down. Maybe it is the discovery date, or the sound of a text or his tardiness after work. We want you to visually assign a picture or a cartoon or a visual image of the trigger. If you are triggered by dates...draw a calendar that is missing that specific date. If the sound of the text triggers you because you saw the affair partner's text during discovery, change your text sound to something that makes you smile. When he is chronically late, create some tickets for his tardiness that entitles you to a gift of your choice or a bouquet of flowers or a massage without sex.

WE KNOW THAT YOU CAN'T IMAGINE MAKING LIGHT OF THE TRIGGER BUT THE TRUTH IS THAT THOSE ASSOCIATIONS ARE OF THE PAST, NOT THE PRESENT, AND YOU CAN KEEP THEM IN PERSPECTIVE BY CHANGING THE MEANING OF THEM.

How would your life be different if you learned how to manage the triggers instead of the triggers managing you?

The brain is a powerful tool and your trauma triggers can be organized so that you are aware of their presence, but you are no longer a hostage to them.... It takes creativity to view them differently.

THE STOP METHOD

Deepak Chopra shares a powerful technique to stop unwanted thoughts called The STOP Method. The next time you feel a trigger think:

- **S** = Stop and notice the feeling.
- **T** = Take three deep breaths and smile. When you feel a trigger, the LAST thing you want to do is smile. After the 3rd breath, smile as big as you can. Next, feel the smile flutter from your mouth down to your toes.
- **O** = Observe how the body feels to experience the smile flutter. The mind can't feel a trigger and a smile at the same time.
- **P** = Proceed with Care, Compassion or Kindness. You can either do something nice by creating some self-care or paying it forward by calling a friend, baking cookies for the kids or paying the toll for the next person in line.

Not only will The Stop Method interrupt the effects of the trigger, it will also move you forward in your day.

Before you throw out this effective exercise, try it three times and notice the powerful impact it has on your psyche. Don't underestimate the power of your thoughts to change the effect of how it affects you.

Another way that you can manage the triggers without the help of a partner or support person is to try the following:

1. Identify what you believe that you are noticing in your own body when you are triggered and tell yourself that your main goal is to stay "in the here and now." You then ask, "Why am I triggered?" If you can't identify the trigger, give yourself permission to accept that the trigger must be linked to the past and you are in the present.

2. Find ways to stay grounded to the here and now by orienting yourself to the present. Look around the room and notice 3 things that bring you comfort. Maybe it is a picture on the wall, the softness of the comforter under your hands, or the image of your child smiling. Remind yourself that you are safe and nothing bad is happening now.

3. De-escalate the experience by saying something nurturing and safe. "I am not in jeopardy right now this "very" second and nothing is putting me in harm's way."

4. In this step you can take 3 to 5 deep breaths and tell yourself that you are working through the trigger that was in some way "linked" to the past and that what you can control is the present moment, and in the present moment, "you are safe." Congratulations, you have gone through the trigger busters cycle by staying in the moment and being your own coach!

CHAPTER 5

Accountability and Integrity

YOUR OWN PERSONAL BOUNDARIES WILL HELP PROMOTE SAFETY

Your Values Accountability Check-In

What we know about partners is that if they attend to their feelings, take time to be in the present, and hold themselves accountable to some very important values around self-care, self-reflection and boundaries, they will feel more confident and self-assured and better able to meet their needs.

First, it is vital to acknowledge and feel the feelings, but know that you are not your feelings! Feelings are not facts. They are a deep expression of your past and present experience because of your circumstances but are not necessarily facts. They are fluid and will change daily if not hourly.

The following checklist will help you hold yourself accountable and treat yourself with integrity. When focusing on yourself, you will find that it is most important to be true to yourself. As simple as that sounds, it can be difficult to commit to writing in your journal every day. This workbook is a place for you to practice being authentically honest without fear of conflict arising. It allows you to take a deeper look at who you are as a woman as well as who you want to be.

Look at the following guidelines for accountability and integrity as well as for communication. Circle the statements that you believe you do well. After you have circled those strength areas, go back and star (*) the areas that you want to improve. What we know to be true is that the more you practice these techniques in your journal, the more likely you will be able to honor the woman you are and communicate authentically to determine what boundaries and consequences you may need to work through partner betrayal.

GUIDELINES FOR ACCOUNTABILITY AND INTEGRITY

- Take responsibility for yourself.
- Speak your truth.
- Assess your behaviors and determine whether they are helpful or hurtful to you.
- Do your personal best.

- Give yourself permission to rest and relax and pursue intentional self-care.

GUIDELINES FOR COMMUNICATION

You will have a better sense of integrity if you communicate honestly with others and use the following principles as a guideline for being true to yourself.

- **Practice Assertiveness, Use Your Voice.** It may be unnatural at first to be assertive, but the more you practice this skill, the easier it becomes. The betrayal may have caused you to communicate more aggressively. This is a common response to the "fight response" of trauma. Assertiveness is being clear and direct about how you feel, what you need and what you believe. We will talk more about assertiveness in the pages to come.

- **Be Aware of Feelings.** Work toward expressing them. Because avoidance of feelings is so ingrained, give special attention to how you feel and express yourself with feeling statements such as "I feel happy" or "I feel afraid." This may feel too vulnerable. It is courageous to share your feelings but as Brené Brown says, "Only share your vulnerability with people who have earned the privilege." If it is not safe to share your feelings with the betrayer, you will need to find other people with whom to express your feelings. Support groups are great for sharing feelings.

- **Be in the Here and Now.** Emphasize the present. As much as possible, focus on your experience of the here and now. This can be especially challenging because the pain is in your past but believe it or not ... your strength is in the present and you can keep yourself safe by staying in the moment. There is much research that shows that the happiest, most content people are those who stay in the present. You deserve to find your happiness again. We tell partners, "Don't let him rob you of your joy."

- **Use "I" Statements.** Rather than using the editorial "we" or "you," speak for yourself: "I feel angry."

- **As You Self-Reflect, Avoid Asking Questions.** It is natural to be in that state of confusion as to how could this have happened to you and why did he do this to you? You are trying to make sense of a situation that makes no sense! It is not until you learn about addiction that you figured out that you had nothing to do with his choices, yet his choices affected every fiber of your existence. Do your very best to stay away from the whys. "Why?" leads to analyzing and often leads away from emotions. Before asking the question "Why?", consider the statement behind the question and then express the direct statement. For example, instead of asking "Why am I always wanting more explanation from him?" ask yourself, "What do I need to feel safe with him?"

> *It is not until you learn about addiction that you figured out that you had nothing to do with his choices, yet his choices affected every fiber of your existence.*

- **Avoid Self-Judgments, Be Descriptive.** Describe what you notice about yourself and be aware of your self-critical statements. If you find you are judging yourself, stop and gently give yourself permission to restate your observation, allowing room for imperfections. Partners typically wonder what they could have done to have prevented his acting out. They wonder why they were not good enough to have kept him faithful. Do not place blame on yourself. Your marriage may not have been perfect, but it was not the reason for his acting out. Be gentle with yourself and accept your imperfections. They did not contribute to his sexual addiction. For example, instead of saying or writing, "I must not have been good enough sexually" say "My husband had a sexual compulsion that had nothing to do with me!"

As you are doing the work, remember to:

- **Guard Your Confidentiality.** Keep your journal in a safe place where you can be assured that no one else will read it without your permission. You have likely looked through his recovery materials to stay safe and understand why this happened to you. You know how tempting this is, so please...keep your journal in a safe place.

- **Be Prepared.** After discovery, it is common to often walk through life in a half-dazed state, unaware of your needs or feelings. Transforming your life requires you to be alive and attentive. Be prepared to work hard and be enthusiastic about the changes you will make. Stay focused on you!

- **Create Support.** We are social beings. We were not designed to be isolated in our lives—especially during a crisis. It makes sense that you may have wanted to hide this betrayal and his addiction from everyone. It is very important to find safe people to share this information so that you will not feel so isolated. Betrayal recovery groups can often be helpful to share intimate details of the betrayal. 12 Step groups can also provide free support. Plan to create a support network or build on your existing network to ensure that you have people who will be able to encourage you.

THIS IS YOUR LIFE!

Commit yourself to making changes
as if your life depended on it!
The best way to predict your future is to create it!

Connect with Your Inner Self

MEDITATION PROVIDES A SAFE PLACE TO CHANNEL YOUR INNER KNOWING

Guided Meditation

Guided meditation is a form of visualization that allows you to experience your own internal process. Due to the trauma it can be difficult to calm down the brain and make space for reflection. Your complex situation stole your sense of safety and lead to racing thoughts and full-fledged panic. It can amplify your anxiety and set you into a downward spiral. Partners complain that they want to stop the rumination that is the natural by-product of being triggered by sexual betrayal.

Even though it seems impossible to do something like meditation because it feels like your brain will never calm down, with practice it can be the antidote to slowing down the brain and working on learning not to catastrophize. We happen to believe that meditation allows you to connect to your intuition and your relationship with your higher power, the universe or God. When you have a stronger connection to yourself and spirit, you are more likely going to be "inspired—in spirit" to see the world differently and to behave differently...with more confidence and certainty. Landing you right into posttraumatic growth!

Many partners experience problems that are initially rooted in childhood issues. This visualization intentionally takes you back to your childhood so you can connect with your emotions as well as begin to develop a sense of hope that you can provide healing and support on your ongoing journey through your adulthood wounding of partner betrayal.

We have created a meditation that will put you in touch with issues surrounding sexuality, womanhood, depression, and the need for support. The clear and embedded message is this:

> *"Your life can be different, and you can create the support you need!"*

You may understand this on a conscious level and act on it immediately or you may need to grieve the loss of what you never had as a child. Simply allow the unconscious to imagine how you can take care of yourself presently and learn from what you did not get as a child. Many partners who have experienced partner betrayal are also grieving the ongoing trauma of having a lifetime of struggles. This meditation reinforces the power within all women and the intuitive process you possess to make the needed changes in your life.

- Set the atmosphere as you prepare for this meditation.
- Find a time when there will be no interruptions and you can spend ten to fifteen minutes quieting your thoughts.
- Dim the lights, light a candle and choose some soothing soft background music.
- Read over the meditation included on the next page.
- Then, close your eyes and focus inwardly, quietly listening to what is within - see what images, words, feelings and thoughts surface as you reflect on the meditation.
- You may choose to record the meditation yourself, or ask a friend to record it for you, as it may be soothing to hear your friend's voice guide your inward journey.
- If you have a tendency to disassociate, you might ask your therapist to assist you in doing this meditation.

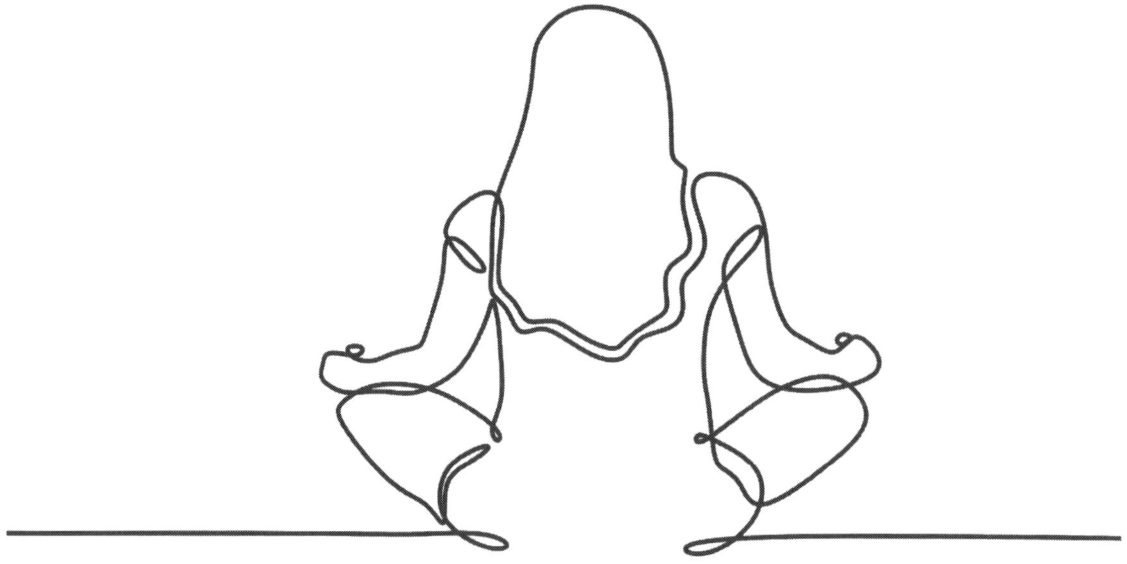

THE MEDITATION

This is an opportunity for you to quiet your thoughts and find that place of centered stillness that allows you to get in touch with all of your wisdom and your knowledge, taking this opportunity to listen to what is deep inside. It may feel uncomfortable at first because of your ruminating thoughts, but the more you practice quieting the mind, the more you will find the serenity you deserve.

Take some deep breaths and imagine a color that you can breathe in that represents strength, love, and a gentle knowingness that you have everything you need to manifest all that is deep inside. The feminine process is an amazing gift that you were given. To be a woman has afforded you the special gift of growth, intuition, and relationship building. You have the ability to be so attuned to the needs of others, yet this is your time to listen to the needs that are within you to recharge and replenish. How would your life be different if you started to regularly attend to your own needs and wants, and if you put yourself first so that you regularly had more to give? Who might you become?

Think back to what it was like to be a young adult, an adolescent, a school-age girl, or perhaps a toddler learning to take her first step. Find a safe place to visit each one of those stages in your awesome development. Who was there for you? What was that person like, and what did they do to reassure you that you were perfect just the way you were? We all have someone who has been that special person...go back to that place now and experience that person and the support that was given to you. What would it have been like if you could have received a steady stream of encouragement? What might you have done?

How you might have viewed your life differently had the different stages of your life been celebrated for the life experience that you incurred?

Imagine what it would have been like to have your family celebrate the feminine process as your body began to change and develop. Imagine that the instrumental people in your life were there for you and took you out to celebrate the beginning of your menstrual cycle. How might that have affected your womanhood?

When you turned eighteen, what events took place to shape the woman that you had become? Although there was much to learn, how did it feel to come into your own and realize that you had decisions that were solely yours to make?

And now that you are a woman who has come into your own, how might you do things differently so that you can feel the well-deserved feelings of accomplishment, contentment and self-love? This may seem insurmountable based on the sexual betrayal that you have experienced but you are absolutely capable of recognizing your strengths. As you move into that contemplative season of life, can you be the kind of woman who can support and validate yourself like you do others? Because the true essence of being a woman requires that you nurture yourself with the same attention that you use when you take care of others.

How might you right some of the pressures you may have put on yourself for not being enough? There may have been times when you have not felt (fill in the blanks…attractive or smart or strong enough) ________ in the past? You have been through so much, but it is time to self-nurture and discover your brilliance. "You were born to make manifest the glory of God which is within all of us." What if you were finally to know that you are absolutely perfect the way you are? All the things that you have viewed as imperfections are really what have helped you develop the character to be the woman you are today. If there are things in your past that have tormented you or made you sad, as an adult woman you have the capability to release them from your spirit and move on in your journey.

And there may be wrongs that you feel that have been done to you that you are not sure that you will ever be able to release, and you can surrender those whenever you believe that they are holding you back.

Allow yourself the opportunity to be imperfect and release all the pain, burden, and sorrow that you have experienced because of addiction so that you can see yourself with more self-love and assuredness. You can accept yourself more unconditionally and smile with a gentle knowingness that you are all that you were meant to be, that your worth does not depend on your accomplishments, nor does it require that your legacy be known to all. Instead, your brilliance is because you have done the best you could and the hardships you have faced are a result of other people's actions. You have made a difference in the lives of others who you have loved. Now it is time for you to put yourself first and really focus on intentional self-care.

Accept that you are enough, no matter what has occurred in your life. You can be the woman you have strived to become because your focus has changed and you are putting you first!

Take some deep breaths, breathing in the feeling of contentment and peace and breathing out the feelings that overwhelm you.

Breathe in the strength that is deep inside and exhale the overwhelming feelings of the day. Breathe in the light that you have always had and breathe out the darkness of the day. As you begin to return to this room, this space, allow yourself to begin to hear the outside sounds around you, the noises of the room, the sound of your own breathing and anything else that is occurring outside of your meditative space.

We recommend that you read the meditation out loud and record it in your voice memos so that you can listen to it daily to remind yourself that you are powerful beyond measure! Feel free to change and customize this in any way that brings more serenity, self-assuredness and love.

Feel free to change and customize this in any way that brings more serenity, self-assuredness and love.

JOURNAL YOUR INSIGHTS FROM THE MEDITATION

Journal your thoughts about the meditation. What are you being guided to feel, see or do? Perhaps you are being encouraged to employ something that promotes better intentional self-care. You may be nudged to change something about you or your environment. You may have gained some new insights into your pain and/or your recovery. Spend some time reflecting how this meditation may change you.

Write your thoughts down here.

USE A TRANSITIONAL OBJECT TO ANCHOR YOURSELF

You may ask yourself, "How do I attain more confidence and self-assuredness to be the person I want to be?" We have found that you can process your life better when you have the proper structure and support in your life.

This means you need to organize your life to allow for time to journal on a consistent basis, find quiet time to reflect and contemplate and create an environment that encourages you to take care of yourself.

- Do you journal regularly? Journaling allows you to stay focused on you.
- Do you have a picture that captures your love of life or energy?
- How about some refrigerator magnets of quotes or pictures that remind you of how strong you are?

TRANSITIONAL OBJECTS

Transitional objects help you move through the stages of change. They bring a sense of security and stability. They remind you of who you were but more importantly, who you are now or who you are becoming.

- One woman bought a new mirror and put it in her entry way so that as she left or entered her home, she could glance over at the mirror and say one of three things to herself daily. She would say, "You are going to have a great day today" as she left the house. She said that she wanted to set the intention that she could and would find things to be grateful for in her daily living. She would also say, "Don't forget God loves you" to remind herself that she was not on this walk by herself.

- And when she needed a little mental boost, she would encourage herself and say, "You showed up today and you did a great job."

That is why we urge you to create ways to remind yourself of your uniqueness and worthiness. We would ask you to find an object that represents the new woman that you are or are becoming.

One woman bought a crucifix that reminded her that she could keep the faith. Another woman bought a sculpture of a woman with two faces that reflected her many feelings. Another woman bought some stained-glass art to remind her of the beauty in life.

You may want to find a piece of art that speaks to you of your strength or find a special poem or writing that honors you.

Be sure to include the things that you have been creating in this workbook! Framing the "Name Game" artwork or placing your vision board somewhere that you can see it are great reminders of the "What is a Woman?" exercise—As a woman I want to be: ________________________. Those visual reminders provide inspiration.

We all need things that inspire us. What inspires you?

____

____

____

____

____

You need inspiration to work through the tough stuff and release yourself from your anger and the conflict that you have felt about the betrayal. The next section will inspire you to work through residual feelings from your past.

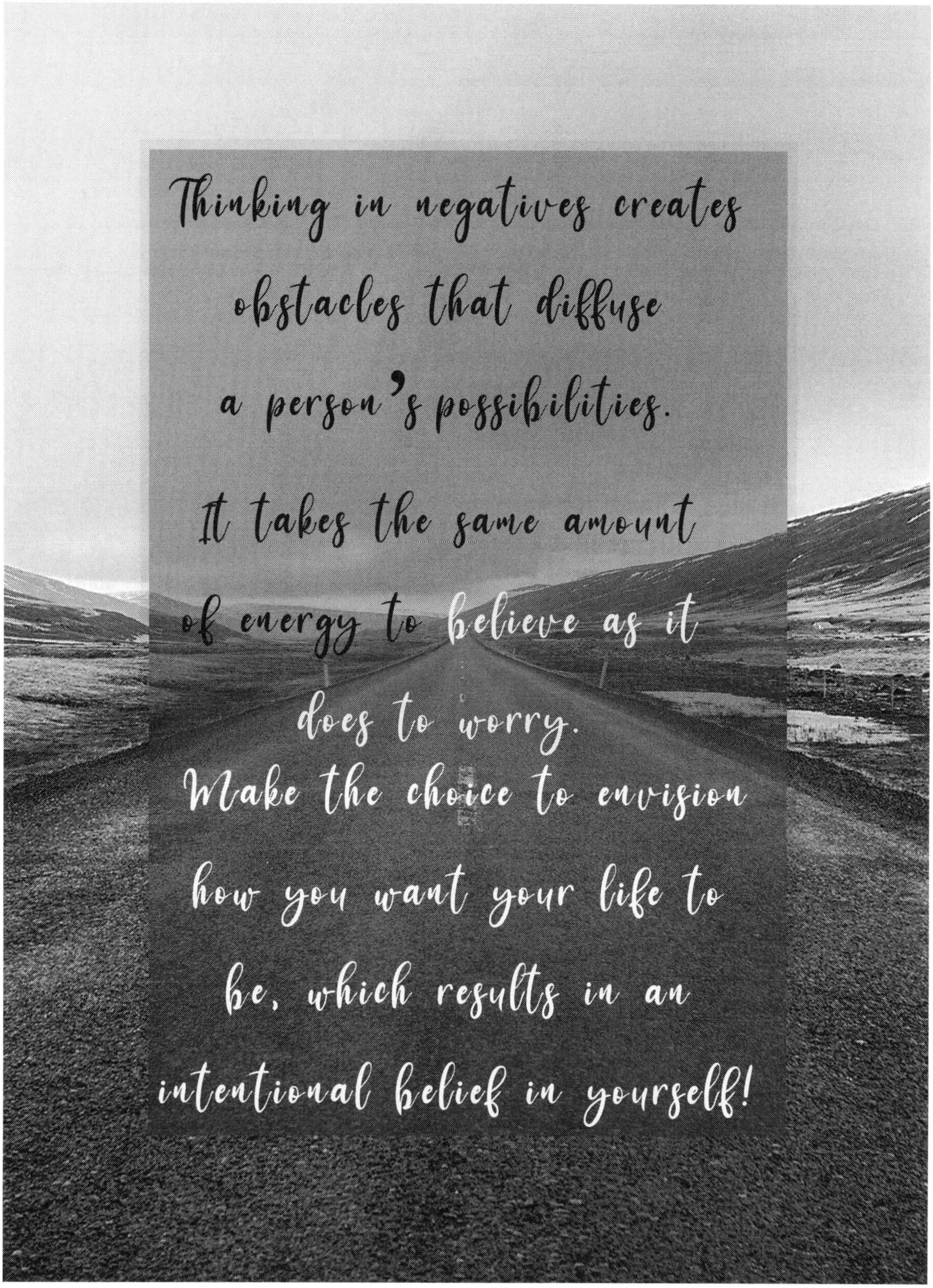
Thinking in negatives creates
obstacles that diffuse
a person's possibilities.
It takes the same amount
of energy to believe as it
does to worry.
Make the choice to envision
how you want your life to
be, which results in an
intentional belief in yourself!

Phase Two

WORKING THROUGH THE ANGER, GRIEF AND MOURNING

CHAPTER 7

Power of Self

CHANNELING ANGER AND CONFLICT INTO POWER BY IDENTIFYING YOUR ANGER, MOURNING YOUR LOSSES AND GRIEVING WHAT IS

How to Identify, Work Through, and Grow from Conflict

Partners need to feel their feelings and honor the anger, sadness and loneliness the infidelity has caused them to feel. There are many exercises that can help release you from the betrayal and assist you in recognizing the wisdom and power you have gained from examining your core issues. This section includes exercises that will address overt and covert anger, past and current abuse, fear of conflict, poor self-esteem and trauma.

When you work on these exercises, you will break free of old behaviors and create new ones like the following:

- Interrupting self-defeating patterns about the betrayal and focusing on your resiliency
- Creating self-awareness so that you can interrupt unhealthy behaviors and intentionally create alternative healthy behaviors
- Learning how to accept conflict versus personalizing it and feeling inadequate, inferior, and unworthy
- Establishing accountability to yourself which promotes a commitment for change

These exercises are intense and many psychological layers will be excavated through this journey of self-exploration. Many partners may feel resentful that they have to do this intense work to free themselves from the bondage of partner betrayal. We know that not only is this work necessary to work through Phase 2, it can also process some earlier wounds in your life that you might not have addressed otherwise. These exercises give you an opportunity to validate your feelings and own them. You can become extremely honest with yourself to create strategies to change your life in dramatic ways.

The exercises presented in this chapter are a compilation of processes we have experienced in our own personal development as strong women and in our professional work with women who have been through trauma. As you are journaling, let your imagination, creativity and strong intuition guide you!

Here are some of the themes you will be exploring:

- Attachment issues
- Partner betrayal
- Boundary setting
- Assertiveness
- Self-mutilation and self-destructive behaviors
- Body image issues
- Abandonment
- Conflict avoidance
- Over-responsibility
- Self-hatred

YOUR JOURNAL IS A SAFE CONTAINER TO PROCESS YOUR LOSSES WHILE DOING THESE EXERCISES

Trust is a basic, yet vital need of all individuals. If you have grown up in an environment that was unsafe physically, sexually or emotionally, your trust in others has been breached. When your husband became the betrayer, it affected your sense of self. It is likely that you no longer have trust in yourself, your spouse or the world as you once knew it. You doubt that all the answers you need lie within you. His betrayal stole that from you and now, by doing this work, you are reclaiming your identity, your intuition and your spirit as a woman!

This workbook becomes a safe "container" for you to do your work. It will guide you through your feelings of loss, grief and anger.

As you utilize these techniques and exercises, take time to journal your feelings to process them and grow stronger from them. Journaling is a safe way to identify feelings that because of the betrayal have blocked you from your own empowerment. The betrayal robbed you from believing in yourself and now it is time to take back your power and trust your feelings and your intuition again!

Anger Exercises

Many women who have been sexually betrayed struggle with depression or anxiety. Nature and nurture both play a part in these conditions. We know there is often a genetic link to depression and anxiety, and that these conditions may also be situationally or environmentally induced. When a woman experiences betrayal, she begins to doubt her own ability to discern the truth. The good news is that, regardless of their origin, there are many ways to treat these conditions. Exercise, healthy diet and support are among your first lines of defense for overcoming these struggles. For those who suffer more chronically, counseling along with medication may be instrumental in treating your depression or anxiety.

One of the most important aspects of feeling sad or fearful because of the betrayal is to acknowledge the emotion of anger and even rage that is locked up in you. Since we know that depression can also be "anger turned inward," it becomes important to acknowledge the repressed or suppressed anger inside. You may have trouble seeing how you are doing this, but we know that trauma affects you on a cellular level and releasing the emotions allows you to move on in your life and not stay stuck in your anger, sadness and grief. This correlation is eloquently described in Bessel van der Kolk's book, The Body Keeps the Score. He explains that when trauma occurs, the body keeps the score to keep you in a state of high alert as a protective signal to keep you from being hurt again. The important thing is to create safety and acknowledge the pain so that you can move forward in your life. That is why you have to do the work.

You will be releasing the adult betrayal that is current time. This work will also address earlier abuse. If you experienced abuse as a child, it may be that you were not encouraged or permitted to express your anger. You may have incurred many traumatic events like parental alcoholism, abuse or emotional neglect. This journal is a safe place to begin "connecting" with the missing emotional link in your life—YOUR ANGER!

Acknowledging and expressing anger allows you to emotionally purge, which often provides a much-needed catharsis from the anger you may have carried around for years or even decades. If you are one who denies feeling any anger, we encourage you to consider what injustices have occurred prior to the sexual betrayal. You may find that this brings up repressed and suppressed anger, often from childhood trauma or from being raised in a home where anger was not an acceptable emotion to have or express.

If you had a normal childhood, it will be necessary to identify and own the injustice that has occurred because of the addiction. Expressing injustice unleashes the natural by-product of anger.

Anger work is intense, powerful and liberating! For some, just talking about the emotion and referencing anger work can create anxiety and will send you running. You must prepare for this work by realizing that anger is normal and necessary. When expressed directly and in a non-destructive way, anger can have a positive impact on your life.

Anger is simply a buildup of adrenaline and must be released. It is that energy that protects us in a fight-or-flight situation. Anger is vital to our survival as individuals and as women. You deserve to release your anger about the sexual infidelity and all the wrongs that have impacted your life!

YES-NO: THE POWER CONNECTION

The first anger exercise is "YES-NO." It will allow you to begin to feel the power of your anger.

Because anger is often internalized, close your eyes for a moment and internally identify your core issue that relates to feeling dismissed, devalued, disrespected, etc. Write down your core issue. Take your time in order to clarify your core issue. It may be about sexual addiction or a childhood issue. You may want to focus on issues pertaining to your job, marriage or other aspects of your life that have played out due to your recent discovery. Once you have written down your core issue, you are ready to move on.

First, write words that finish the statement related to your core issue. When listing YES statements, you are making proclamations of your value, strength and power. There may be several people that come to mind who have violated your values, so you may need to make several lists. Here are some examples:

- YES, you will respect me!
- YES, I have the right to expect you to be faithful to me!

- YES, I will be heard!
- YES, I deserve to know the secrets!

What do you need to say YES to? It may be about your childhood or it may be about the betrayal. List them below:

- YES, ____
- YES, ____
- YES, ____
- YES, ____

Now consider the other side—NO. When listing NO statements, you are making declarations of your personal, emotional, and physical safety and boundaries. Here are some examples:

- NO, I won't allow you to betray me without consequences!
- NO, you won't gaslight me!
- NO, you won't tell me what to do!
- NO, I won't permit you to victimize me!

What do you or did you need to say NO to in regard to the sexual betrayal or because of your childhood? List them below:

- NO, ____
- NO, ____
- NO, ____
- NO, ____

Next, take a moment to recenter yourself. Close your eyes again and reflect on the phrases "I WANT IT" and "YOU CAN'T HAVE IT." Internally focus on your core issue in your past or in the present and what each phrase empowers you to think. As thoughts and feelings emerge regarding your core issue, write them down as well.

See what the "I WANT IT" statement may reveal. Here are some examples:

- I want my serenity back!
- I want to be in charge of my boundaries!
- I want my power!
- I want my self-esteem back!

What do you WANT? List them below:

- I want ____
- I want ____
- I want ____
- I want ____

The "YOU CAN'T HAVE IT" may exemplify:

- You can't have control!
- You can't have my love!
- You can't have my trust!
- You can't have my innocence!

What belongs to you that NO ONE can have? List those things below:

- You can't have __________________________________
- You can't have __________________________________
- You can't have __________________________________
- You can't have __________________________________

Oftentimes in life, women are told that their thoughts, feelings and beliefs are wrong, and that the other person is right. Finish writing about the ways your thoughts, feelings and beliefs belong to you and are right. You have the right for new boundaries and consequences now that the betrayal has occurred. It's a validation and declaration of self-esteem! Women who have been betrayed often feel a sense of confusion and bewilderment that their vows have been destroyed. They say things like, "I can't understand how he could have done this to me." Or, "I would never have allowed infidelity into our marriage." Or, they shake their heads and say "How could he have had sex with someone else, I can't imagine him ever thinking this was ok. Who did I marry? I could never have done this to him…EVER!" When a woman has these thoughts, she is comparing herself to her husband and she usually keeps locked inside the comparison of her values vs. his values. The next statement "I am right" captures the hurt and indignation of knowing what is right vs. wrong and wondering how someone could have done this to her and to their marriage. Many women say, "I was a good person and I could NEVER have done this to him."

What statements do you need to declare that should have been honored in your relationship with your spouse?

- I'M RIGHT
  - I'm right to have honored our marriage.
  - I'm right to have avoided all temptations.
  - I'm right to have expected your love and fidelity.
  - I'm right to despise you right now.

What would you say I'm right to?

- I'M RIGHT
  - I'm right ______________________________
  - I'm right ______________________________
  - I'm right ______________________________
  - I'm right ______________________________

In what ways would it be helpful to assert yourself and declare that what he did was wrong…dead wrong? When you make this statement "YOU'RE WRONG," you are proclaiming the obvious. You are voicing your truth that his actions were inexplicable and that you had nothing to do with the behaviors that he chose. This statement is especially helpful if there have been slips and relapses in his recovery. You may understand that his addiction kept him powerless in making the right choices, but once an addict knows what recovery tools will enable good choices and decisions, he is dead wrong when he doesn't use them! Recovery, when lived rigorously, will create the man you deserve.

- YOU'RE WRONG!
    - You're wrong to have deceived me.
    - You're wrong to spend time with prostitutes.
    - You're wrong to have gone to strip clubs.
    - You're wrong to have endangered my life.

What do you need to say?:

- You're wrong ______________________________
- You're wrong ______________________________
- You're wrong ______________________________
- You're wrong ______________________________

Often, women take this writing and reflection to the next level. After completing your writing, you will likely feel a renewed sense of personal power. Feeling the power of your insights and awareness can be truly liberating. Although it is quite simple, there are several steps to take to physically experience this newfound power.

To experience this exercise more fully takes five to six minutes. The primary goal is for you to feel the power of the words physically and emotionally that you have written. You will need the following:

- A safe/support person (such as a close friend, family member, or therapist) who is not afraid of intense expression of emotion—your therapist may be willing to facilitate this experiential exercise with you and your safe/support person.

- A safe place where you can get as loud as you need to be
- Drinking water
- Tissues

Your safe person needs to be willing to be your partner in a volume exercise, which will require her or him to also yell loudly. Begin by asking your safe person to stand face-to-face across from you. Some women place a piece of tape on the floor between themselves and their partner to visually represent a safety line. Remember that your anger is normal and necessary and is not meant to be destructive. Also, remember that as you get loud with your safe person, you are not yelling "at" that person; rather you are finding your voice and your power.

> *As you get loud with your safe person, you are not yelling "at" that person; rather you are finding your voice and your power.*

As you face each other, be certain to stand solidly on the floor with your feet shoulder-width apart. Ask your partner to push on your shoulders to make sure you are not a "pushover." If you are, replant your feet so you are standing firm.

With your arms uncrossed, both of you are to look into the left eye of the other, as the left eye is said to be the "window to the soul." This helps both of you to get grounded and to know that your partner is supporting you through this exercise, and you are doing the same in return.

Review your written list, then close your eyes as you visualize the betrayal or another core issue. Although your partner has likely not written a list, she can gain more benefit to also close her or eyes and connect with a core issue as well. Based on your comfort level, you may choose to state your core issue out loud to your partner or just keep it safe within yourself. Once you are clear about your core issue, you are ready to begin. You will be starting with the word "YES." Throughout the exercise, your partner will match your volume, answering only with the opposite word or phrase.

Once you begin, you will say only one word: YES or NO! This allows you to stay focused and clear, and to feel and hear your own power. Each time the "YES-NO" is exchanged, the "YES" increases in volume. The "NO" responds at the same level, though not getting louder or overpowering the "YES." It is like watching children arguing, "YES"–"NO," and on and on again. The person who will be saying "YES" starts.

It is very common to find that you are unable to get loud at first. Think about two children arguing to visualize the intensity that is possible. Give yourself permission to get as loud as you can, allowing yourself to "raise the roof off the building." Another typical response you may notice is that you or your partner smile or become tearful and cry. Know that this is natural, but work hard not to smile, as it will take away your power. Also, work hard to "push beyond your tears," as tears can reduce the power or strength of the message you are trying to convey. Your partner may also need to signal you with a thumbs-up to encourage you to raise your volume and get louder. If your voice is coming from your throat, you will cough and it may feel like you are choking. If that happens, place your hand on your abdomen and bring your volume up from your diaphragm, not your throat. You may also find it helpful to allow a guttural or primal sound to emerge from your body.

As the exercise continues and you both become louder and more comfortable with your word, then switch. You had been saying "YES," so now it is your turn to say "NO." You may focus on the same core issue, or you may find that a deeper one may have emerged during the process. The "YES" person once again begins the process. Naturally, the energy and intensity will die down and you both will stop. Now you will begin by stating "NO," and again you will be determining the volume.

The experience continues with the next phrase that you wrote about. Review your list, close your eyes to center yourself on the words you wrote, then choose which phrase you would like to start with:

- I WANT IT!
- YOU CAN'T HAVE IT!

Again, as you find the energy and intensity naturally dying down, stop, change phrases, and start again. Take drinks of water in between rotations as needed.

Repeat the same steps outlined above for the next phrases:

- I'M RIGHT!
- YOU'RE WRONG!

We teach women that physically externalizing depression and sadness allows them to transform depression and sadness into energy. Our belief is that depression and sadness are usually the result of unexpressed anger. When physically released, the anger is more useful. Anger is an energizing agent due to the adrenaline it produces. When women feel their energy and adrenaline, they can mobilize their lives differently and accomplish personal goals that are empowering and life-changing. It can feel exhausting to spend hours and hours in your own ruminating thoughts, wondering what your options are and how you might execute them. Resourcing "the energy from anger" becomes motivating and will help you identify and implement your choices.

Once you have expressed and externalized your anger, you will be more likely to discard and detach from it, which allows you to move into the acceptance stage of your grief. Grieving and mourning affords you an opportunity to examine and release yourself from the pain. This may lead you into the "forgiveness stage of letting go" by releasing your anger.

We do not believe that you need to forgive your spouse. Only you can make this decision. This is a very individualized decision and can only be made if you feel moved to take that next step. However, releasing your anger allows you to release some of the trauma from your past. This does not mean that you forgive the person who wounded or harmed you, but it means you no longer allow the anger to hold you back from being the person you want to be or from accomplishing the things you want to accomplish in your life.

When you liberate yourself from your feelings of anger, you are more likely to naturally move into an energetic state that will contribute to you making some important decisions. Only you can decide if and how you will do that. We believe that the process you create will be exactly what you need to take you on your journey of self-discovery.

RACKETS AND PILLOWS: EXTERNALIZE THE ENERGY

Typically, after doing a YES-NO exercise, you may want to "physicalize" your work. This is simply a way for you to connect with your power literally and physically.

THE PROCESS

We ask you to kneel in front of two or three stacked overstuffed pillows. For safety purposes, it is best to have a safe/support person with you. Additionally, remove any rings or other jewelry.

Focus on a core issue that has created a trauma, injustice, or betrayal in your past. Common themes other than the betrayal include sexual abuse, parental abandonment, divorce, disrespectful children, authoritative employers, chemical dependency, etc. As difficult as it may be to conceive, this exercise will liberate you from the power that others have had "over you." This allows you to recognize the powerful force your anger has been for you. Unfortunately, your anger has most likely locked you into your feelings as opposed to releasing them. When you externalize the anger, you are no longer limited by internalized fear, and you automatically take charge of your life with confidence and assuredness.

When you beat on the pillows with a tennis racket as hard and as loud as you can, you become increasingly in touch with the energy moving through your body. We also would encourage you to use a word that speaks directly about your anger. Some women groan, growl, curse, or speak short sentences (such as "I hate you! You are a bastard! You can't control me!").

Although most women can externalize their anger in five minutes or less, you should beat the pillows until you are completely spent, with no energy left. After you feel like you have no more energy left within you, we would ask you to beat the pillows ten more times to push beyond the fatigue. Oftentimes, this is the most powerful part of the exercise because you utilize stored-up energy that has been inaccessible for years.

When you are finally done, you may even have blisters on your hands, symbolizing the work you did. Repeated anger work may result in your being fortunate enough to have destroyed your pillow with the innards coming out—if so, tell yourself that these innards are the "guts" of your anger and keep a part of them to remind you that you have externalized and released your anger.

PROCESS THE WORK

After you have completed your work and before you retire for the evening, answer the following questions:

- where in your body do you feel energy?

  ____

- what color is the energy?

  ____

- what adjective best describes how you feel at this moment?

  ____

This is a type of anchoring that has its roots in Neurolinguistic Programming (NLP) and can be helpful in honoring the processing that you have just done.

It is so important to do this work and know that in no way were you ever responsible for his deceptions or his actions. Sometimes this work has been done in treatment centers and partners have reported that after the hard work, they were left feeling like they in some way contributed to his actions and his choices. This work is to process your feelings and you were not responsible for what he did!!! You did not know what depths he was pursuing in his addiction and you must never take on ANY responsibility for his addiction despite what he may have said, or what a professional might have told you or even a 12-step support group might have inferred when they told you that you were a co-addict or codependent.

> *You must never take on ANY responsibility for his addiction.*

INTEGRATION

Write a short paragraph describing your experience. This work will create a shift in you, so we recommend that you write several times this week about how your life is different now that you have released the anger. You will be extremely sore and/or emotionally raw, so it is critical for you to set up some self-care behaviors in this next week.

Releasing the anger has...

The thoughts I had after doing the exercise were...

I feel stronger now that I have done the exercise because...

I will practice self-care by...

I will respond differently to the addict by...

Alternatives to Racket Work

If you have a physical limitation that prevents you from doing racket work, you can tear up books or catalogues instead. As you rip the pages, verbalize your feelings and then rip through more pages. It takes great strength and energy to tear fifteen, twenty, or thirty pages at one time. The sound of the pages ripping, combined with the power such action requires, provides a therapeutic way to release pent-up aggression.

VESUVIUS: EXTERNALIZATION OF ANGER AND DEVELOPMENT OF PERSONAL BOUNDARIES

You need a listening friend as a support person for this exercise. "Vesuvius" is an exercise that was initially developed for couples. It has been adapted from "PAIRS." We have found it to be a tremendous exercise for a woman, because it allows you to release your anger and experience the support from a listening friend whom you have asked to assist you in this exercise.

This exercise encourages you to get in touch with suppressed or repressed anger. Women are often taught that they should not have ugly, angry thoughts and feelings. Often a partner will feel afraid to share her story for fear of repercussions from others. This keeps your emotions in a suppressed state and to really grieve your loss requires that you visit all your emotions in a safe way.

You have been so surprised at how angry, rageful and out of control you have been since discovery and you likely have thought that you are going crazy because this is not who you ever thought you can be. Ask how might you use your anger to motivate you to set boundaries or use your voice? Remember, that you are likely in the "fight" mode and your brain has gone offline. This is the worst thing that has happened to you and when you channel that anger it may ramp up your anger initially but later the externalization will give you a sense of serenity and calm.

THIS EXERCISE IS FOR YOU IF YOU ARE REALLY, REALLY ANGRY!

Not only will you get to spew your feelings, you will get some uninterrupted time to say whatever is locked inside of you. This exercise gives women permission to identify their feelings and to erupt like the ancient volcano, Vesuvius.

PURPOSE OF THE VESUVIUS

This ritual allows for the emotional purging and spewing that needs to occur when your anger has been suppressed and repressed for years or even decades. If you are tired, frustrated and enraged, you will find this tool a safe way to unload, uncork, explode and erupt. It is done with permission and for an allotted amount of time. The following steps outline the Vesuvius process.

THE PROCESS

1. You request a certain amount of time to vent your anger, frustration, and rage. In most cases, this exercise requires three, five or ten minutes. (You will likely find that when you have uninterrupted time to say what is really on your mind, you will not need as much time as you would think to find your voice).

   You will need to find a support person to silently be a witness to your anger. This person is called the "container," because she or he metaphorically holds and contains your anger. This person also serves as the timekeeper and tells you when your time to vent is up.

2. Your listening friend will be learning and practicing how to contain your anger without internalizing it. She or he is asked to visualize a Plexiglas shield, a Teflon coating, a wall or any other protective mechanism that allows her or him to avoid internalizing the anger that is spewing forth. It may be beneficial to internally speak a mantra such as, "This is not about me."

3. You begin by verbalizing your anger regarding a core issue. Here you emote your dark, ugly and judgmental feelings. Nothing you say during this period must be true, fair or politically correct. Yelling, screaming and even cussing (if you are so inclined) are common, expected and encouraged. Many times, as you share your anger, your

issue will deepen, or your focus will shift to another person to whom the anger is directed. Many women have experienced that as they are yelling, their anger shifted from their unfaithful husband to their mother or father because of trauma experienced in childhood. **(Please note that this is natural and does not take away from the anger you feel towards your spouse, but it does link together the ongoing trauma that you may have felt your whole life. This may originate in early childhood trauma that results in complex post-traumatic stress).**

4. Once you have emotionally purged or after time has run out, you thank your listening friend for safely containing your anger. Then, it is vital to "de-role," acknowledging that she/he is not "my husband or father or mother," but she/he is "my friend who has contained my anger or kept my confidence." Your listening friend then uses reflective listening to acknowledge that she/he is not the role that she/he played by saying "I know I am not your husband, father, or mother, but I am (name), your friend and someone who cares about you."

5. After you and your listening friend debrief, you can share with each other what it was like to be in this exercise.

Survivors of sexual betrayal, sexual abuse or other forms of trauma often find this exercise frightening, yet freeing, because they can say whatever they want to the perpetrator(s), no matter how violent or graphic. Remember, if you are the listening friend during this exercise, you are not there to console or shut down your friend's feelings. You are there as a neutral person to "contain" the emotions...nothing more and nothing less!

SEXUAL ABUSE AND OTHER TRAUMAS

One in three women report experiencing childhood sexual abuse. Consequently, you may have experienced a trauma that is blocking you from being everything you can be. For this reason, it is imperative that you address any trauma or trust issues that stem from this abuse and neglect. Exercises that focus on empowerment provide the strength necessary to help you move from victimization to survivorship.

Processing pain is good for the soul!

Staying stuck in the pain is not!

As you know, bad things happen to good people all the time. Enlightened people will want to work on processing these events so they can understand them better and grow from them. That is truly one aspect of living a good life. When trauma occurs, it is so very important to acknowledge the feelings and work through the pain so that you can make sense of your world and redirect your life in a purposeful way. This will move you into posttraumatic growth.

We work with lots of women who have experienced additional trauma besides partner betrayal. In many cases, the initial trauma occurred in their childhood and they did not have the support or resources to help them resolve it as it was happening or directly afterward. Again, the trauma might have been from living with an alcoholic parent, being physically, emotionally, or sexually abused, or living in chronic poverty. If people aren't given the opportunity to process and work through their trauma, there is high likelihood that they will re-experience it again in different ways. Until it is understood and resolved, the trauma will return again. As a woman who has experienced childhood trauma, you will need to work through the trauma. Once you have worked through the issues, you will undoubtedly feel stronger, healthier, and better able to use the skills you have learned from resolving the trauma to improve your life. This typically means that you also must go through the process of anger because it allows you to let the trauma go and move on. Quite often, the person you feel that you need to forgive is yourself, as many women blame themselves for being victimized. Many women blame themselves for not knowing their husband was acting out. Know that you had no idea that he was betraying you and you are in no way responsible for his actions. You may blame yourself, but channeling your anger may help to release this self-induced blame.

> *You had no idea that he was betraying you and you are in no way responsible for his actions. You may blame yourself, but channeling your anger may help to release this self-induced blame.*

It is the process of letting go that will encourage you to find meaningful ways of growing and contributing to life so that you feel good about yourself.

All the great theorists say that it is the suffering that promotes human beings to grow into people who are fully actualized and evolved. We know you are reading this and may be saying, "Why do we need to experience so much suffering to actualize growth?" Well, what we believe to be true is that trauma causes suffering which creates great transformation that actualizes you and leaves you wanting to improve your life and the lives of others. You acquire a sense of purpose. If one does not deal with the past pains, one cannot learn and get healthier. If you don't work through the pain, you will likely stay stuck and blocked from allowing good things to come into your life. It is not fair that partner betrayal became part of your life, but use it to become stronger. Many women have used the suffering to make amazing changes in their life!

As therapists, we never believe that you should sit in the anger, so we are dedicated to offering "Anger Exercises" that move you through the anger so that you can feel the grief, do the mourning and move into your next chapter with or without him. We are saddened to watch clients who may avoid conflict, anger or the resentment that naturally builds when one avoids the conflict. Just know that the work that you do makes you stronger, wiser and more self-actualized!

You are over halfway through this book and you have done some serious work! Now it is time for you to reflect on any pain that has occurred prior to the infidelity.

TIME FOR REFLECTION

What pain from your childhood continues to haunt you?

How do you believe that this experience or trauma has blocked you from growing?

How has it shown up in your life again in a different way?

How have you sought out support and resources to help you work through pain?

How has your suffering made you stronger?

List other ways that you have grown emotionally or spiritually.

And if you have been trying to do this on your own, you have more than likely felt alone and isolated. If this is the case, are you willing to seek out support and resources to help you work through the pain now? This may be even harder work for you to "receive" from others. Although this can be really difficult for you, we promise that when you create more opportunities for encouragement, it will build the environment you need to grow.

You deserve to get healthy and release yourself from the pain. There are so many resources, organizations and groups that are available today so you do not have to walk through this pain alone. Get some help so that you can heal and use your past to strengthen the future! But please go to a "partner sensitive" organization or counselor because many therapists, support groups and institutions have not been trained in partner sensitivity.

In the back of the book, you will find some helpful resources to enable you to build support.

Now, let's move on to other exercises to acknowledge the pain and to help you produce strength

Letters

In therapy, partners are routinely asked to write a letter, role-play or create a script or play to re-enact the trauma, then provide an ending or resolution piece that empowers them and allows them to put to rest the long-standing issues. If you had a magic wand, what could you envision for your future? How would you like your relationship to get stronger? There is nothing wrong with hoping for the future while processing the many losses this addiction has robbed you of in your relationship. And if you don't believe it is possible to forgive him and move forward, then ask yourself, "what would it look like if I left the relationship and moved on?" It can feel so scary to contemplate these decisions, but no matter what state he has left you in, you are in the driver's seat with how you proceed from here.

It may not feel like you have many choices, but when you are working through your feelings your writing and rescripting will allow you to own what YOU want in your life. When you do this, you are much more likely to make it happen. Not only are you sending a message to your higher power that you know what you need in your future, you are also enlisting your brain to get onboard with the direction you want to go next. The old brain/primal brain does not know the difference between your vision and reality and some resolution or peace that can be achieved.

> *When you re-enact your future through scripting or vision work, you are sending a message to your higher power that you know what you need in your future and you are enlisting your brain to get on board with the direction you want to go next.*

WRITING YOUR DECLARATION LETTERS

If you choose to write a letter, we recommend writing three letters of a different nature: (1) an irrational, angry, hostile, ugly letter, where you will bring up all of the hateful and vengeful thoughts that you have had about the betrayal (if you have suffered earlier childhood trauma, we recommend separate letters for each trauma); **and** (2) a letter that serves to reclaim your survivorship and move beyond being a victim. In this letter, you tell him what you will or will not tolerate now that you are aware of the deceit and the betrayal. A third letter is beneficial to allow you to reflect on the lessons you have learned from being a survivor.

LETTER 1: THE VENOMOUS LETTER

After describing the trauma and its effects, you are encouraged to be angry and to let your "shadow side" take over. You may tell the betrayer(s) that you want to castrate him, or that you hope he dies alone, or that you hope he gets cancer and it eats away at his body. Even strong faith-filled women have periodic moments of rage and anger and they experience ugly thoughts in response to the betrayal. To acknowledge the venom you feel allows you to release it so that it doesn't fester and keep you from moving on in your life. We know that acknowledging the anger allows you to move beyond it. The important thing is to acknowledge all the thoughts and feelings that you have had in the past for cathartic purposes. Our experience is that catharsis is extremely beneficial in resolving sexual betrayal and does not promote violence. Again, this is a very liberating experience, releasing the pent-up feelings you may have been feeling your whole life.

LETTER 2: THE SURVIVOR LETTER

The second letter is a rational, direct, assertive letter telling the betrayer your feelings and the consequences of his actions. This helps to reclaim your strength and to move on from the event. You will want to include the boundaries that you have enforced to keep yourself safe and the consequences if they are violated. Finishing with the rational letter helps you to reclaim yourself as a strong survivor and to provide closure. It further allows you an extra opportunity to regain composure. Therefore, it is always necessary to finish this activity with the second letter.

LETTER 3: THE RESILIENCE LETTER

The third letter highlights what you have learned and what has carried you through as you talk to your past-self from the perspective of your present-day self. The truth is that you already have wisdom to share about what has carried you this far in life. This is a tough letter for partners to share because they are not quite sure how all this wounding has served them and made them stronger and there is a tendency not to own their strength because they do not want to legitimize in anyway what he has done. We understand your possible hesitance and yet acknowledgement of your resilience is absolutely necessary to move forward and to prevent you from experiencing further abuse from the betrayer or from anyone else in your future!

Devote some time to writing and responding to the following:

I am stronger now and this is what I appreciate about my resiliency...

TELL YOUR STORY

WRITE YOUR SCRIPT OR PLAY

Sometimes it is helpful to write a play or dialogue to re-enact the trauma/betrayal and then create an ending or resolution piece that empowers you and allows you to put to rest the long-standing issue. Some partners spend several weeks doing this, finding themselves blocked to this process. If you get stuck in this way, we suggest connecting with a best friend and asking her to co-write it with you. Such a friend can offer a fresh perspective that helps you script out the piece together. She will also validate your experience and normalize your feelings. Working with a friend will both help you complete your script and provide you with extra support. You can also take this to your partner-sensitive group for help. Through this experience, you may develop a bond with your friend or group that deepens your relationship! Not only is it cathartic to create a script or play about the wrongs of sexual betrayal, but you also deepen your sense of trust with your support network.

CHAPTER 8

Exercises that Promote a New Sense of Self Awareness

Conflict: A New Perspective

Conflict can be difficult. Most people were not taught how to handle conflict effectively, and so it can evoke lots of uncomfortable feelings. You are most likely either someone who avoids it at all costs or someone who goes for the jugular so you can "get them before they can get you." Oftentimes in therapy, we teach women to practice assertiveness when they are angry with others, working through ways that they can share their feelings, thoughts and beliefs with clarity. Being assertive does not mean that they get what they want, only that they can be sure they were clear and direct about their feelings related to the conflict.

Working with conflict will make you stronger and will help you define boundaries that are so necessary in working with the addict.

In the process of sexual betrayal, your spouse may be discouraged that your healing is slow. He may infer that it is time for you to "get over it." This may leave you feeling insecure and inadequate. You sense his tension and the conflict.

We ask you to learn how to detach from the conflict and remind yourself that you have every right to take as long as you need to process the pain that he caused. We are going to teach you a model to use when he or anyone else is angry with you. It will help you avoid "taking on" someone else's discontent or anger so that you can move forward in your own pursuit of serenity.

FEAR OF CONFLICT EXERCISES

What we know to be true is that women have been taught to suppress conflict. By and large, women are not socialized to externalize anger. Most women either internalize the conflict and ignore it, or become frustrated by it and act out. Women are not usually taught to express it directly.

The following exercises provide a way to practice the skills of expressing conflict and/or not personalizing it. It is based on the belief that you will manage conflictual situations better if you don't personally internalize it. Freud theorized that **"90% of all conflict is projection,"** meaning that most conflict is usually about the other person.

What have you been taught about conflict?

____

____

____

____

____

More than likely, you were not taught how to assert yourself and deal with conflict directly and honestly.

Both of us have made it our personal mission to teach partners not to avoid conflict, but to recognize that it is normal, natural, and necessary. In healthy relationships, working through conflict can build intimacy.

If you are dealing with someone terribly dysfunctional or unhealthy, then handling conflict without personalizing it will keep you from taking it on and feeling like you are responsible for someone else's feelings. Partners need to depersonalize the conflict they feel from their spouse and detach from his arguments. Oftentimes a spouse will use DARVO or GASLIGHTING to keep you from recognizing his addictive behaviors, and he will turn the situation around and make you feel like you own the problem.

DARVO is an acronym coined by Jennifer Freyd to describe a common strategy of abusers. Unfortunately, addicts naturally use it to hide their addiction by blaming you for some part of the problem.

Your spouse will do the following:

- D = Deny that there is really an issue. "It didn't happen."
- A = Attack the person who needs clarification. "You are crazy or You are the one with the issue."

- R = Reverse the roles. "You are chronically suspicious and need to get help."
- V = The addict portrays himself as a victim. "You always turn this around on me and I really can't take this."
- O = Offender The addict says that you are the offender and you are accusing him. I am tired of you being so cruel."

GASLIGHTING is when your spouse denies the truth and works diligently to make you feel like you are imagining the issue or the problem. This leaves you feeling as if there is something wrong with you or that you own the problem. Partners start to doubt their own sense of reality and feel as if they are going crazy. Both of these techniques are common responses to keeping you from holding him accountable for his behaviors.

THE FOUR TOOLS OF CONFLICT: HOW TO DEPERSONALIZE FROM AN ADDICTS NEED TO DEFEND HIMSELF

Whether you are living with an addict who is in good recovery or you are dealing with an addict who frequently slips, relapses or refuses to get into recovery, it can be exhausting to see him fall back into periods of denial. When this happens, he will often do what it takes to maintain that all-important state of denial, either out of ignorance (he doesn't even know that he is lying to himself), or to protect the addiction at all costs. Often times he will create conflict to keep you from holding him accountable for his addiction. This can be in the form of denial, gaslighting or using DARVO. To stay out of the trap of needing to rephrase, defend, explain or profusely protect yourself, we advise using this conflict approach when he incessantly berates you for holding him accountable.

The conflict model that we will be talking about has some very unusual components and will need to be practiced so you get comfortable with this approach. The model entails working through four steps.

When someone is angry with you, recognize the person's criticism and ask yourself the following question:

1. How did I contribute to this conflict? Maybe you confronted him. Perhaps you became argumentative because you sensed something

wasn't right. Recognize your involvement and remind yourself that you did indeed contribute to the problem, however, tell yourself that you will only own 10% of the conflict. Validate what you did and take responsibility for how you managed the conflict. There will be times that YOU mishandled the situation and it will be important to own that and assure the other person that you won't make the same mistake again.

2. Remember that 90% of the conflict is really about the other person. In other words, the sender of the conflict is struggling with something and is projecting it onto you. Therefore, it is important to recognize that your spouse's need to put you down, argue with you or be critical of you comes out of an unresolved issue within him. You then tell yourself, "This is not about me; this is about my spouse." Say it over and over to yourself (silently, of course).

3. Tell yourself that you are not going to let your spouse's anger get to you. You may even want to say, "I won't give him the power to make me feel ____________________ (a feeling word like hurt, angry or inferior)."

4. The last step is to reinforce that you have faith in one of three things:

    - Faith that you are strong enough to weather the conflict.

    - Faith that you and your spouse will resolve the issues. This will allow you to approach your spouse with a neutral attitude. If he refuses to forgive you or work with you, then you must recognize again that this is HIS issue.

    - Faith that you believe in something greater than yourself, and surrender the conflict to that power, whether that is God or the Universe or your Higher Power. Know that surrendering does not mean giving in, it means that it will ultimately get worked out in a way that will hopefully give you some resolution. This allows you to not internalize the conflict and therefore be less affected by it. It also reminds you that there is something greater than you who can support you through these tough times.

Imagine these scenarios:

- Did your spouse act suspiciously when you entered the room? Did he close his laptop, shut off his phone or act as if you startled him in some way? Your gut says his behaviors were suspicious. You angrily inquire about his behaviors. He calls YOU suspicious and complains that he has no privacy. All of a sudden, it appears that he is using DARVO and he is the innocent party (victim) and you are the perpetrator. You can see that you are not going to get him to empathize with your concerns, so you use your conflict model to detach from him and his accusations. Using this model deflates the power behind his words.

There are many opportunities to use this model in situations that don't involve addiction.

- In normal situations, have you ever had a fight with your spouse where hurtful and unfair things were said? Later, your spouse apologized and said, "I didn't really mean those things." If you had used this new approach regarding the conflict, you would have not internalized the situation. Once the argument was over, you could have calmly decided what useful information you were able to gain without feeling personally wounded by the verbal attack.

- Has your boss ever taken you aside and made statements that inferred that you were a disappointment as an employee? You were perplexed because you were trying your hardest and doing your best and you knew darn well that although not perfect, you were an excellent employee!

Adopting this model means that you look for opportunities to improve your performance and simultaneously realize that your boss may be under some pressure to get the employees to sell more or produce faster. This approach to conflict helps you to hear the evaluative remarks without allowing them to affect your self-esteem or self-worth.

When you use this approach, you will walk out of the encounter with an awareness and with your self-esteem intact. When you refuse to take things personally, you are not as defensive. This allows you the gift of insight, because you will know what you need to do to improve the situation. Conflict will no longer scare you. You won't take on the criticism.

PRACTICE USING THIS 4 STEP MODEL

Think of a specific incident that involved a conflict with your spouse.

____

____

____

____

____

APPLY THE 4 TOOLS OF CONFLICT

1. How did I contribute to this conflict? Maybe you confronted him. Perhaps you became argumentative because you sensed something wasn't right. Recognize your involvement and remind yourself that you did indeed contribute to the problem, however, tell yourself that you will only **own** 10% of the conflict. Validate what you did and take responsibility for how you managed the conflict.

   ____

   ____

   ____

   ____

   ____

   ____

2. Remember that 90% of the conflict is really about the other person. In other words, the sender of the conflict is struggling with something and is projecting it onto you. Therefore, it is important to recognize that your spouse's need to put you down, argue with you or be critical of you comes out of an unresolved issue within him. You then tell yourself, "This is not about me; this is about my spouse." Say it over and over to yourself (silently, of course).

   Why is 90% of the conflict about him?

   ____

   ____

   ____

   ____

   ____

   ____

3. Tell yourself that you are not going to let your spouse's anger get to you. You may even want to say, "I won't give him the power to make me feel ____________________(a feeling word like hurt, angry or inferior)."

   Why will you NOT allow his feeling get to you?

   ____

   ____

   ____

   ____

   ____

   ____

4. The last step is to reinforce that you have faith in one of three things:

    - Faith that you are strong enough to weather the conflict.
    - Faith that you and your spouse will resolve the issues. This will allow you to approach your spouse with a neutral attitude. If he refuses to forgive you or work with you, then you must recognize again that this is HIS issue.
    - Faith that you believe in something greater than yourself, and surrender the conflict to that power, whether that is God or the Universe or your Higher Power. Know that surrendering does not mean giving in, it means that it will ultimately get worked out in a way that will hopefully give you some resolution. This allows you to not internalize the conflict and therefore be less affected by it. It also reminds you that there is something greater than you who can support you through these tough times.

How does this 4th tool of conflict apply to you and how can you use your belief in God to get you through this conflict?

____

____

____

____

____

____

Although using the concepts of this model may feel foreign to you at first, in time you will likely find that you become less afraid of conflict, which makes you more objective about its reality. This approach teaches you that all-important skill: not to take things so personally. It is as if you are coated with Teflon and you will be detached from feeling bad about yourself!

Look for opportunities to use this approach and notice how liberating it is to put the situation into perspective. Conflict will become a tool to understand the other person better, which helps in assessing what you need to do to protect yourself. As the relationship gets healthier, it will also help in the relationship-building process.

ASSERTIVENESS: DEVELOP YOUR COMMUNICATION BACKBONE

As a partner, it is especially important to stand your ground in the relationship. You spent many years being in the dark because of his secrecy and deceptions and now that you know better, you can assert yourself and set up expectations and consequences.

The good news is that you are not alone. We work with people from all types of backgrounds and lifestyles, and consistently see one commonality, especially among women. Women come into the office and lack the ability to assert themselves with others. Most women don't know what assertiveness is, let alone know how to use it. If they do know how to do it, it is because they have seen an important person in their life assert him or herself on a regular basis.

Assertiveness is standing up for your beliefs. It is being clear about what you think and how you feel. When you are assertive, you let others know your intentions, and you stay true to yourself so that you can achieve your goals and move closer to what you need. Unfortunately, it is not a guarantee that you will get your needs met, but it is affirming when you communicate clearly to avoid any self-doubt or gaslighting. Assertiveness is conveying a direct message about your needs. It is proactive and it empowers you to change.

What is your definition of assertiveness?

____

____

If you want to have better self-esteem and get your needs met, you must learn how to assert yourself. We call it developing your backbone—the backbone of self-esteem.

Which person are you? *(Circle the statements that apply to you)*

- Do you assert yourself with your spouse?
- Does he know how you feel and what you think?
- Do you speak about what is on your mind in a direct, concise manner?
- Does he know the real you and what you stand for?
- Does he know your bottom line?
- Do you let him know when he is using DARVO or Gaslighting in an attempt to get you to stop communicating with him?

Or:

- Are you afraid to share feelings for fear of a conflict?
- Are you concerned that he may leave if you share your bottom line?
- Do you squelch your opinions because you think they aren't important or you are afraid they will be shot down?
- Are you afraid to speak your mind because if you do, your needs may not get met and you will feel rejected?
- Are you fearful to speak your mind because you fear that he will use your words against you and it is just not worth the energy?
- Are you exhausted by the discovery and don't have the energy to further communicate with him?

Which person are you? It's important to be honest so that you can have the awareness and know when to make the needed changes. Are you more like the first example or the second?

Most women have never received any formal assertiveness training. This workbook will help you to polish and practice your assertiveness skills.

Oftentimes partners who don't assert themselves get walked on or they find themselves putting their needs on the back burner. They will also doubt their communication which leaves more opportunity to doubt themself. Assertiveness keeps you out of the victim role. It lets him as well as other people know where you stand.

Many "life strategists" stress that you teach people how to treat you. When you assert yourself, you teach others about your feelings, limits, and boundaries. You no longer can get walked on because you have changed your behavior.

There are two basic formulas you can use to assert yourself. Both involve using "I" messages. Begin by thinking about something you have kept to yourself and then practice using one of these sentences to share your thoughts. Take a moment now to fill in the blanks below:

ASSERTIVENESS STATEMENTS

1. ____________, when you ____________________
(person's name) *(behavior)*

I feel ____________ because ____________________
(feeling word) *(the message it sends me, or the message I hear is)*

____

2. I don't like ____________________, and this is what I'm
(behavior)

going to do about it if it occurs again ____________________
(statement of action you will take)

____

HERE ARE SOME EXAMPLES OF ASSERTIVENESS:

- A wife of 15 years finds out that her recovering husband is gaming after she goes to sleep. She believes that this is another form of addiction and has asked him to speak to his counselor about his behavior before he plays again. Her husband says he will shut down his gaming and wait until they talk to the counselor but then is caught gaming at 2:00 A.M....again.

  The wife asserts herself by stating, "Andy, when you disregard my request and hide your gaming from me by waiting until I have gone to bed, I feel fearful because the message it sends me is that you are exhibiting your old addict behavior which alerts me to the possibility of a relapse.

  I can't control your behavior, but I will ask that you sleep in the other room so that I am not awakened when you come into bed late from gaming.

- The newlywed tells her husband, "When you tease me about my failed attempts at taking care of the house, I feel angry because what I hear is, I'm not a good housekeeper."

- The mother of three came into the room and found her husband sending lewd messages to an affair partner. She very clearly said to her husband, "I am no longer going to tolerate your acting out behavior. I am going to help you pack your things, ask you to go live with your brother. Then I am going to begin attending a support group for people who have husbands with compulsive acting out behaviors. You are an addict and I will no longer tolerate living in the same house with an addict."

The important thing to remember about assertiveness is that it is about you. It is not used to change others. Many partners complain that their assertiveness will not get their husbands to change. That is exactly right—being assertive is simply about letting him know how his behavior affects you, and it is one step closer to you changing yourself. Being assertive does not guarantee that the other person will change; it means that you are being strong and direct about how you think and feel. The exciting part of assertiveness is that once you are clear, you feel better about you. Consequently, you work on doing things that will move you closer to getting your needs met.

USING THE ASSERTIVENESS FORMULA

As an experiment, think of one thing that you have kept inside and not shared with your spouse. Using the assertiveness formula, practice filling in the blanks and imagine yourself saying that statement to your husband. Be sure to write the statement down, which will make you more likely to use it in your daily life.

1. ____________________, when you ____________________
(person's name) *(behavior)*

I feel ____________________ because ____________________
(feeling word) *(the message it sends me, or the message I hear is)*

____

2. I don't like ____________________, and this is what I'm
(behavior)

going to do about it if it occurs again ____________________
(statement of action you will take)

____

1. ______________, when you ______________________________
(person's name) (behavior)

I feel ______________ because ______________________________
(feeling word) (the message it sends me, or the message I hear is)

____

2. I don't like ______________________________, and this is what I'm
(behavior)

going to do about it if it occurs again ______________________________
(statement of action you will take)

____

1. ______________, when you ______________________________
(person's name) (behavior)

I feel ______________ because ______________________________
(feeling word) (the message it sends me, or the message I hear is)

____

2. I don't like ______________________________, and this is what I'm
(behavior)

going to do about it if it occurs again ______________________________
(statement of action you will take)

____

1. [ ], when you ______________________________
(person's name) (behavior)

I feel ____________ because ______________________________
(feeling word) (the message it sends me, or the message I hear is)

____

2. I don't like ______________________________, and this is what I'm
(behavior)

going to do about it if it occurs again ______________________________
(statement of action you will take)

____

It takes practice, but we guarantee that the more you practice it, the easier it will be to create and use assertiveness statements. And, what we know most of all based on our work with thousands of women, is that when you concentrate on changing yourself and not others, you speed up the process of getting what you want and need.

TRUST EXERCISES

Trust comes from being honest even in the face of conflict. When you trust, you can share your emotions honestly. Assertiveness is when you can share those feelings honestly. But assertiveness can cause conflict. If your spouse is developing good addiction and relational recovery, he will be someone you can assert yourself with, share your emotions with openly, grow and begin to redevelop a trust that he will honor those feelings and emotions.

We have met many women whose trust was violated as a child; therefore, they did not allow themselves to trust easily or ever again. When a second betrayal occurred, it immobilized them and discouraged them from trusting themselves or the world.

> *Sometimes the wounds run much deeper because after partner betrayal, you no longer trust him, yourself or the world. This may have even affected your trust in God.*

Answer the following questions to assess your "trustability." Trustability means that you can rely on someone's strength, ability or integrity. You have a confident expectation of something; hope. As you heal, you should look for people whom you can trust, and more importantly, you should begin to trust yourself and your faith again.

Are you someone who has trouble trusting others? If so, why?

____

____

____

____

List previous experiences that have seriously affected your ability to trust.

1. ____

2. ____

3. ____

4. ____

How has trauma affected your ability to trust yourself?

How has partner betrayal impacted your ability to trust the world?

How has his sexual addiction caused you to doubt your spiritual beliefs, your God, your church?

Do you believe you will ever be able to trust again?

What would need to happen to believe that you can trust again?

Have you been able to trust others in the past who initially violated your trust?

If so, what enabled you to trust them?

Perhaps you pick people who treat you kindly, or who sit next to you at family functions, or who have something in common with you, like having an alcoholic father.

It is important to recognize patterns in those that have hurt you. Doing this requires that you use your intuition and life experiences. As Dr. Maya Angelou said, "When people show you who they are, believe them the first time." This means it is YOUR responsibility to protect yourself from people who consistently hurt you.

When you love an addict, you will likely experience many woundings. If he is working towards good recovery, there will be times when he falters. He won't be perfect in his recovery journey and this will hurt you and cause you to detach from him. Detaching with love is a natural process that protects you and keeps you guarded from his struggles.

To increase trust will require that he consistently works on recovery and over time gets healthier in his behaviors. He will falter less, have fewer slips and proceed in helping others work on their recovery journey as well. He will work harder on your relationship, exhibit healthy relational behaviors (i.e. empathy, increased communication, feeling identification and improved intimacy). If he is struggling with the relationship, he should read *Help. Her. Heal. An Empathy Workbook for Sex Addicts to Help Their Partners Heal*. It is likely that your spouse will need relational skills that he does not possess at the present time.

Let's examine the complex trauma that you may be experiencing because of past woundings in your life. Are there people in your life who have consistently hurt you? If so, who are those people? Write their names below and explain why you continued or still continue to allow this to happen.

We are not saying that as a child you were responsible for allowing someone to violate your trust, however there may currently be people who are unsafe and continue to criticize, condemn, or disparage you as a woman. You can set healthier boundaries to insulate yourself from their abuse.

NAME	PATTERN OF ABUSE	REASON FOR ALLOWING THE PATTERN OF ABUSE/MISTREATMENT

This workbook is designed to help you see patterns that you want to break. You'll need the help of a partner-sensitive therapist or coach to change unhealthy patterns. If you find yourself consistently allowing your spouse to hurt or take advantage of you, find a specialist to help you break this pattern. If you have had a lot of trauma in your life, seeking help from a trauma therapist might be a good choice for you.

See the recommendations in the back of the book for people who are trained in partner-sensitive betrayal trauma, sex addiction or trauma.

Women need to feel safety, connection, and trust. Continue to work on ways of finding safe people whom you can form a healthy connection with to develop ongoing trust. If you have gotten this far in your workbook, we know you are making great progress! Building safety, connection and trust takes a long time, so notice your progress and keep the faith that as you grow healthier, so do your relationships!

WHAT FEARS CONTINUE TO HOLD YOU BACK?

As you move into posttraumatic growth, there may actually be a "knowing" that you have many gifts to bestow on others now that you have moved through Phase 1 and 2 of partner betrayal. You may be asking yourself how you might help others or contribute something to the world?

In Phase 3 of posttraumatic growth, you may want to assess how you want to continue living your life and making a difference.

Consider the following questions:

Is there anything stopping you from living out your life's plan or dream?

____

____

____

Do you have reservations about your own sense of confidence?

Sometimes fear will keep you from doing the things you need to do to sustain real change. Could any of these fears be getting in your way?

- Fear of Failure.
    - I have experienced failure in the past when...
    - I believe it held me back because...
- Fear of Embarrassment.
    - I am most embarrassed when...

- Fear of the Unknown.
  - What I fear most is...

    ____

    ____

    ____

- Fear of Rejection.
  - If I become successful, I fear that I will be rejected because...

    ____

    ____

    ____

- Fear of Hurting Others.
  - If I achieve my goals, I am afraid that I will be hurting ____________ because it will make him or her feel...

    ____

    ____

    ____

- Fear of Success.
  - If I were successful, I would fear...

    ____

    ____

    ____

If fear is holding you back, it's time to face your fears head-on. We recommend that you share your fears openly and honestly with a family member, a mentor or a friend you genuinely respect. Sometimes just talking about it unlocks the fear. If not, you may need to talk to a therapist or life coach to get you past the stumbling blocks. If your fears are deeply rooted in your childhood or past pain, a therapist would be most appropriate. If your fear is about feeling unable to create a strategy to make your dreams happen, a personal life coach can help you create that plan to move out of your comfort zone.

Don't let fear immobilize you from stretching and moving into that new comfort zone. We all know that you can't win unless you play. You have been through so much, and it is time for you to accept that as Marianne Williamson says, " You are powerful beyond measure and playing small does not serve the world." You absolutely have what it takes to move through this world with self-assuredness and confidence!

Accountability Tools to Promote Healthy Behavior in You!

COGNITIVE BEHAVIORAL EXERCISES: THE CHART METHOD

Individuals in recovery track their sobriety time. They know the last time they used alcohol or drugs and they know that their first day clean is their sobriety date—they can tell you they have 30 days clean or 72 days clean or 3 ½ years clean. Charting progress is helpful so you can see all the work you have done and how it has paid off in your life. We find cognitive behavioral therapy (CBT) to be extremely valuable as a concrete way to keep track of your progress. CBT reinforces new behaviors. We recommend using a chart to hold yourself accountable for working on your goals. See pages 153-154 for an example of how to make goal tracking visually appealing!

Visual cues serve as a reminder of your accomplishments. A chart allows you to visually see your success, or lack thereof, regarding your goal. A visual reminder is an extra reminder to hold yourself accountable.

It is easy to get sidetracked when your mental health is contingent on your spouse's recovery. Therefore, you might find it helpful to identify very specific behaviors that hold you back from finding serenity.

Give yourself the assignment to list on poster board how many times you have demonstrated any new behavior. One woman tracked her DWC days, which were her "days without checking." She had spent the first two years after recovery surveilling her husband's phone, phone records, expenses, computer and eventually realized that she did not like who she had become. She decided to use CBT in her women's group and chart her unhealthy surveilling behaviors. This allowed her to see her progress, plus her group held her accountable and encouraged her to stay the course. Groups are an excellent source of accountability and support!

One divorced partner knew she always attracted unhealthy men and vowed to stay out of unhealthy relationships, so she tracked her DWR days, "days without relationship." Her group encouraged her to find other forms of connection that were activity based so she decided to join a gym, take an art class and participate in a bible study. This allowed her time to get to know herself better and release her need for attention from men.

Sometimes CBT consists of changing behaviors. Here are some of the new behaviors you may want to keep track of:

- How many times you have practiced assertiveness?
- How many times you have created boundaries and said "NO?"
- How many times you have not been self-destructive?
- How many times you have not tracked your spouse?
- How many times you have not called your ex-husband?
- How many social contacts you have made in a week?
- How many days you followed your gut?

The Chart Method increases individual accountability. It not only serves as a concrete vehicle to map out your success, it also acts as a visual reminder of progress or relapse.

GROW YOUR RECOVERY TREE

Directions: Write a goal you would like to track at the base of the tree. Write your start date below it. Grab some colored pencils. For each day that you complete your goal, fill one of the leaves with a bright color—red, orange, yellow, green. If you miss your goal for the day, fill one of the leaves with a darker hue—brown, black, gray, etc. The trees contain 60 leaves. Add more branches and leaves as you grow in your recovery! To keep track of multiple goals, make copies of the tree on the next page. Create your recovery forest by pasting the trees onto a large poster board.

Goal:

Start Date: __________ End Date: __________ # Of Days Goal Achieved: ______

Goal:

Start Date: ____________ End Date: ____________ # Of Days Goal Achieved: ______

Body Work

This section of work deals with your relationship to your body. There are many reasons why women struggle with their bodies. If women experience sexual or physical trauma as a child, they will need to acknowledge and process it to promote self-acceptance. If you have been abused, consider doing the following exercise.

BODY IMAGE DRAWING

This can be an emotional exercise and may be best to do with your friend, sponsor, therapist, or coach for extra safety.

Perhaps some trauma has occurred in your life that has greatly impacted your body image. If you would like to assess whether this may be at the core of your inability to "like your body," the following exercise can be helpful to uncover your feelings.

Buy some newsprint paper from an office supply store and ask a friend to come over and draw an outline of your entire body. After you have the outline, draw symbols or choose pictures or words from a magazine that epitomize your self-image, body image and stories that contribute to your sense of self. You may also draw pictures around or outside of the outline to identify past issues, fears or events.

Here are some common areas that you may choose to depict:

- Genitals may be blacked out with an X because of sexual betrayal or earlier trauma
- Empty faces because it felt like you lost your identity as a wife
- Broken heart because the trust has been destroyed
- Eyes may be taped shut from seeing physical abuse
- No mouths because of having no voice as a child, or no power to speak
- Tears because of relationships ending

- Babies that may have been aborted or miscarried
- Genitalia that was blackened out because of STDs

After you complete the drawing portion of this exercise, it can be helpful to write about your feelings. Doing so can be cathartic and can help you better understand how someone may have betrayed you and how this has played out in your body. If this exercise feels too disturbing, it is important to connect with your therapist so you can process it together.

The body does keep the score and it is time for you to reclaim your body. Sexual betrayal does not have to cause irreparable damage, but it does require an awareness of how it has impacted you. And when you look at your issues through a different lens, it can catapult you into naming and claiming what you want to change! Remember, in Chapter 5 as you looked at the Accountability Declaration, we reminded you to:

- Be Prepared. After partner betrayal, it is common to often walk through life in a half-dazed state, unaware of one's needs or one's feelings. Transforming your life requires you to be alive and attentive. **Be prepared to work hard and be enthusiastic about the changes you have made. Stay focused on you! You have done the hard work in this journal to process anger and grief and now it is time to celebrate who you have become. You wouldn't have asked for this ordeal, but you have used it to grow. You are amazing and now it is time to own the woman that has made it to the other side.**

CHANGE HOW YOU SEE YOURSELF: BODY IMAGE EXERCISE

Body distortion is common among women. Betrayed partners inevitably assume that their bodies are not good enough to satisfy their husband's desires. We strive to help women accept their bodies just as they are, regardless of their size or weight. Shame about your bodies only serves to reinforce a negative self-image and this makes change more difficult.

As you release body shame, it is vital to look at your body as a friend. It is important to acknowledge how your body has served you and to appreciate it exactly as it is so that you will create a gentle plan for improving it.

Answer the following questions:

How has my body worked for me?

____

____

____

What do I appreciate about my body?

____

____

____

How might I be kinder to my body?

____

____

____

How can I make peace with my body?

____

____

____

CREATE A CUSTOMIZED PLAN FOR TAKING BETTER CARE OF YOUR BODY

When you are working on improving your body image, it is important to see your body in a new way while you are working on your goals.

Do you have a goal for your body? Instead of being critical, are you able to identify what you like about your body and how it has served you? We encourage you to use the technique of "reframing." Reframing is an important life skill because it encourages you to look at things differently. For example, instead of thinking, "I'm huge" or "I'm fat," you tell yourself that you are voluptuous, soft or curvaceous. This mindset promotes self-love, which in turn promotes self-care. You are more likely to change if you like yourself.

Now that you have the proper mindset, let's get down to business. What specific changes would you like to make to obtain a healthier body? Write down one or two specific things you would like to accomplish and, as you do, keep the following in mind:

- **Be realistic.** We see so many women who want to "weigh the same weight" as when they were married twenty years ago. We would discourage you from picking a weight and suggest that you focus on something other than a number.

- **Think differently.** Use a different word to describe your goal. Do you want to be more physically fit, more muscular, healthier or smaller?

- **Don't make assumptions**. Many partners assumed that their husbands looked at pornography because they were not physically pleasing to him and because they weren't the perfect shape. They put extra pressure on themselves unnecessarily. When they found their husband's "stash or trash" on the internet, they were surprised to find out that their husband liked a body type that was less than perfect. The same can be true of affair partners. Many a woman has found out that their husband's choices were very different than they would ever have imagined. Frequently women have come into the session in disbelief, saying "My gosh, the affair partner was twice his age, or she was overweight or was ugly!" This is not true of all addicts, but it does apply to many acting-out situations. Please don't assume that you would need to change to meet your husband's arousal template. You NEVER need to duplicate or re-enact his preoccupations because they are part of his sickness. Stay true to yourself and stop the comparisons. You have been through a lot!

CREATE A PLAN THAT SUPPORTS THE GOAL

You will be more successful when you think about your goals in small increments. "I will lose one to two pounds this week" or "I would like to fit into my size 14 jeans (instead of the 16's) within twenty-one days." This type of goal can typically be accomplished in a shorter amount of time. Plus, it reinforces positive behavioral changes, making it more likely that you will stick to your goals.

Take steps to cut out one unhealthy behavior and keep practicing it until you have it down.

Work on this repeatedly until you no longer need to think about it and it becomes automatic. For many of our clients, this means they stop eating after six o'clock or they stay away from the vending machines at work.

REPLACE OLD BEHAVIORS WITH NEW ONES

Focus on creating healthy behaviors so you do not experience a sense of deprivation. You will lose weight if you...

- Drink eight to ten glasses of water each day
- Walk for twenty minutes daily
- Stop eating after seven o'clock in the evening
- Eat more vegetables
- Gain more muscle
- Develop a new hobby that takes up "grazing time"

It is important to focus on healthy behaviors to get you to your goal. When you pick a healthy behavior, you pick a healthy consequence. That translates into direct actions:

- When I choose to walk twenty minutes per day, I speed up my metabolism.
- When I choose to write down what I consume, I eat fewer calories.

At the end of each day or week, write down your successes. Reaching a goal requires that you take notice of your accomplishments on the way toward that goal.

The guidelines you have just read are life strategies. Creating a strategy that works for you is thought-provoking and exciting. You will need to integrate these strategies into your daily routine to maintain a healthy lifestyle. As you put together your very own customized plan, remember to pick behaviors that you can practice not just for today, but for the rest of your life.

The goal that I would like to work on is...

My new healthy behavior(s) will be...

One thing that I am doing right is...

One positive aspect of my problem/concern/issue is...

One change I have made this week to get closer to my goal is...

Change Your Thinking-and Your Metaphor

YOUR LIFE CAN FEEL LIKE A METAPHOR

The life of a betrayed partner can often feel out of control, but there are many things that you can do to take back that control and restore your sense of sanity. Many of these things require that you change your thinking. After you have experienced trauma, your amygdala is on hyper-alert to keep yourself safe. However, most partners are looking for ways to restore their own sense of normalcy again. This requires a shift in your thinking. You may be ready to find your new normal, and the good news is that finding your serenity starts with the courage to change the things you can!

Sometimes this happens normally but most of the time this requires a dedication to looking at your life in new ways that will propel your thinking and move it in a positive direction.

One challenge in your current mental health may be the negative chatter that is occurring in your head. If you're having difficulty changing your internal dialogue, you may need to shift your thinking.

One of the fastest ways to create change is to draw a picture or find an image of the problem that represents your greatest fear.

Have you found yourself talking in metaphors about your situation? Do you hear yourself talking about "the garbage" in your life or feeling at the "end of your rope?" Do you tell yourself that this betrayal feels like you are "being run over and over by a mack truck?" I remember one woman telling her husband, "It's like you ran over and over me with your truck and every time you slip, you run over me again!"

This process of speaking in metaphors can happen to all women. We have heard overcommitted women feel like "gerbils on a wheel." Women with chaos in their lives may view that they are "caught in a tornado." Women who struggle with bipolar disorder often identify life as "being on a roller coaster." Some women who do not attend to their own needs may describe their life as a rubber band being stretched to capacity, feeling as though they may snap. Depressed or suicidal women have viewed themselves in a coffin or buried in a cemetery.

Do you relate to any of these images/metaphors? Well if you do, you can change them by revisioning how you feel and what you imagine. We cannot stress how important it is to shift your circumstances by teaching your brain to see differently, think differently and speak differently to yourself!

We recommend that you draw that image, write about it, then draw another image representing what you would prefer to believe about yourself. This simple exercise can help to change the trajectory of your life.

When you speak in metaphors, it can anchor a picture in your subconscious that results in a sense of finality. We work from the presumption that these exercises are a vehicle to unlock your "stuckness," and we believe that when you create a different picture, you will be developing a new neuro-circuitry that will allow you to develop a healthier mindset and catapult you into self-validating thoughts and beliefs about yourself. When you change your thinking, the things around you change. Therefore, by utilizing new metaphors, you can tap into your unconscious and allow a solution to emerge in your conscious thought. The list below includes some examples of exercises that we have found helpful.

CREATE A VISUAL IMAGE OF THE PROBLEM

As noted above, women often speak in metaphors to describe a dilemma. They describe feeling immobilized and stuck in their own situation. We have found that by asking them to create a visual image has helped them move beyond the identified problem. If we were to ask you to find ways to decrease your stress, it could add to the overload you already feel. However, when you create a visual image that is different from what you believe in your psyche, you will naturally "know" what to do to reduce or decrease stress.

NAME THE METAPHOR

Complete the following statements:

My life is like a...

My sexual betrayal can best be described as...

My hypervigilance can best be described as...

My depression can best be described as...

DRAW THE METAPHOR

After you have described your metaphor, spend some time thinking about what that looks like and then draw a picture of it.

Next draw a picture of how you would like your life to be, as it relates to your metaphor. For example, you may draw a picture of a gerbil taking a rest from it's wheel and eating or sleeping; you may depict the calm after the tornado storm; you may choose to illustrate yourself as the operator who controls the speed of the roller coaster, and on and on. The variations of this exercise are endless.

Now notice how your metaphor has begun to shift in your life. Perhaps your tornado has lost its velocity; the coffin may no longer be nailed shut; or the rubber band is not stretched so far.

Your mind is extremely adept at creating change and helping you to get where you want to be, but you must access it in new and different ways to create that change.

Draw Your Metaphor

"WHERE THERE IS NO STRUGGLE, THERE IS NO STRENGTH" - OPRAH

Phase Three

RESTORATION OF SELF

CHAPTER 9

Exercises that Create Restoration & Posttraumatic Growth

Exercises that Create Restoration

Congratulations! You are ready to enter Phase 3 which means that you are ready to focus on yourself separate from the partner betrayal. You recognize that you have grown through the ordeal and that you have internal strengths that have been a part of you all along. Since suffering has resulted in great transformation, you are ready to appreciate your strengths, recognize your progress and use your "capabilities" to make a difference in the world. Your brain is back online and somehow you have actually **grown** through the trauma. You own your thoughts, feelings and beliefs and you are ready to create your own destiny. This section is all about how you can practice proactive thinking to move into the next chapter of your life.

There will still be times when you understandably question your abilities but you will use the tools to move you forward in your life! Many of those tools involve speaking to yourself in kind and gentle ways that promote encouragement and self reliance. It will be so important to coach yourself into reaching your own potential, which includes how you parent, partner and find your purpose and passion. (There are resources in the end of this book that can help you to access your potential).

HOW YOU SPEAK TO YOURSELF

Seeking to grow and expand into your potential requires positive thoughts. Developing the skill of positive self-talk is vital to good self-esteem, but it doesn't just happen. One must practice it diligently because "practice makes permanent."

One of the essential concepts in personal life coaching is the belief that people are born for greatness. Marianne Williamson, author and spiritualist, said it best when she wrote about greatness: "Your playing small does not serve the world."

Dr. Wayne Dyer, in his book *The Power of Intention*, advocates that when we are in alignment with God, we can accomplish great things. To be able to implement our vision or mission in life requires a belief in our potential. He believes that our thoughts create a cause-and-effect relationship in the world. How many times have you said, "I will never be able to trust a man again" or "I'm not smart enough to pull that off" or "I don't have enough money to make that happen"? When you manifest these notions, you project energy that reinforces these negative thoughts—you make them a reality.

Most people have only an inkling of what they are truly capable of. This is in part due to the negative messages they received as children, messages that get internalized and then repeat over and over as one developmentally progresses. These earlier messages deplete them of their uniqueness and then partner betrayal strikes and it reinforces what they already suspected about themselves. How would your confidence be affected if you participated in daily activities or exercises that primed you for greatness no matter what goals you were seeking?

As a betrayed partner, you may be riddled with self-doubt, wondering if you are good enough to keep him satisfied. You may be playing the comparison game, whereby you look at other women and compare yourself to them. It may feel exhausting to constantly question whether your relationship will make it. Can you imagine if you got up every day, looked in the mirror and said to yourself, "Hello Gorgeous...You are going to have a fabulous day!" Then later in the morning, you did some spiritual reading and reminded yourself that you are a child of God and you have everything you need to manifest serenity in your life through your higher power. Later in the day, you listened to an inspirational podcast that reminded you that you have everything within to create the life you deserve. What would it be like to implant those messages into your heart so that you could lose the heaviness of partner betrayal?

Perhaps you could apply it to other parts of your life. For example, if you are a stay-at-home mother, imagine what would happen if you reminded yourself several times each day that you are investing in the most important commodity in the world by deciding to invest in human life—your children. How would your life be different as you moved through a normal routine if you told yourself that the resistance you met with your oldest was normal and natural, and that staying the course assured your child that there were important boundaries in life that needed to be respected?

Or perhaps you are a person whose fears and anxieties keep you locked into the same old job or routine. Imagine what would happen if you spent a month, three months, or a year repeating statements that affirm your desire for a career change or a move to a different part of the country. What if you said, "I am in the process of discovering my perfect job" or "I am well-suited to do a variety of things and believe that there are many opportunities waiting for me"? Would it motivate you to take the plunge and live life to its fullest?

> *Thinking in negatives creates obstacles that diffuse a person's possibilities but utilizing positive self-talk can rebuild your confidence and your self-esteem.*

Women who have experienced trauma are masters at seeing obstacles that prevent them from living their dreams. They may say, "I am not strong enough to do this by myself" or "I no longer believe in myself" or "I could never move away and leave my extended family" or "I have too good of a business to change locations" or "I won't be able to afford the move." Again, thinking in negatives creates obstacles that diffuse a person's possibilities. If that same woman used positive self-talk, she might decide to act on her desire to live elsewhere by checking out the territory, job possibilities and cost of living to create the reality she deserved!

CHANGING YOUR INTERNAL DIALOGUE

It is not unusual after discovery for you to suffer from cognitive distortions. Your self-esteem has taken a hit and you will find yourself thinking things like: "I am not worthy." "I am unlovable." "I am not capable of having a healthy relationship." "I am damaged goods." "I am always settling." It is imperative that you actively change your self-talk so that the distortions don't follow you around for the rest of your life!

- What are your cognitive distortions?

  ____

  ____

  ____

- How has his acting out impacted your self-esteem?

  ____

  ____

  ____

- What is one area in which you lack confidence?

  ____

  ____

  ____

- What are some ways that you can change your internal dialogue and appreciate that area that you have had some insecurities?

  ____

  ____

  ____

It will be necessary, in real time, when your thoughts become self-deprecating, to follow the formula below:

- Each time you find yourself operating on negativity and scarcity, stop yourself.
- Restate the belief in positive terms.
- Make the commitment to change your internal dialogue for ninety days. Ninety days will help to solidify your cognitive distortions.
- Write out the positive changes that occur in your life during that period.
- Make sure to notice how this makes you feel about yourself. You should notice that you begin to have more confidence, regardless of his recovery.
- Recognize that journaling documents the positive changes that you are making in your life!

  ____

  ____

  ____

WORDS SHAPE ATTITUDES: SPEAKING CONFIDENTLY

When we teach seminars on improving self-esteem and self-confidence, we are frequently asked, "What is the number one way to convey a sense of confidence?" One of the most empowering things a person can do is to speak confidently and with authority. Why? Because **"language shapes attitudes"**.

Self-confidence is an attitude or state of mind. Although women typically believe that self-confidence is acquired through accomplishments or achievements, we encourage them to look at self-confidence as a belief in one's self "knowing" that they can handle situations with assuredness and in a capable manner.

If you were to assess the trauma that you have been through, could you imagine seeing yourself as not only a survivor but a thriver? Could you tell yourself that you are the poster child for getting past the betrayal? Do you believe that you will ever be able to move forward and see what happened to you as a catalyst for standing strong and KNOWING your strength? Unfortunately, too many partners do not believe in themselves and choose words that convey their ambivalence.

Does your communication convey confidence? Do you find yourself using words like "I think," "kind of," "maybe," "probably," or "just"? These words minimize the impact of your statements. These words discredit your point of view; hence, people don't take you seriously.

Do you speak with assurance, or do your statements trail off into questions? This negates the definitive nature in the statement. It is important to make declarative statements. Keep your statements clear, concise and to the point. There is no need to say it in a way that requires someone else's validation.

As you examine your linguistics, notice how many times you use words that denote indecision or ambivalence. People frequently use words such as "try" or "think." The word "try" infers that you will make an attempt. Again, this type of speaking sets you up for failure. It sabotages your motivation because it implies that you may not be successful. Don't let the remnants of partner betrayal rob you of your worthiness and your self-actualized goals!

Consider the following statements:

- "I will try to journal."
- "I will try to read my affirmations."
- "I will try to diet."
- "I will try to attend my support group tonight."
- "I will try to pick it up after work."
- "I will try to get more sleep."

Now, take the "try" out of it.

- "I **will** journal this morning."
- "I **will** read my affirmations."
- "I **will** diet."
- "I **will** attend my support group tonight."
- "I **will** pick it up after work."
- "I **will** get more sleep."

This sends both you and the world a clear-cut message. It also makes a statement that you believe in yourself and your ability to get these things done.

It creates confidence, which will make you more successful.

The word "think" has the same connotation: "I think it would be a good idea if..." "I think I will ask for a therapeutic separation." "I think I should consider some medication for my trauma symptoms." Omit the word "think" and replace it with the words "feel or believe" or "plan to or intend to"...then listen to the difference in inflection.

If you lack self-confidence or if you find that these statements apply to you, we encourage you to practice the following:

Ask another person to "time you out" when they hear words like "just," "probably," "maybe," or "guess" or when they hear the words "think" or "try." We frequently use this in our group exercises and find that, on average, people will use these words sixteen times over a five-minute period! This exercise helps to increase awareness and change old patterns. Obviously, once you recognize that you use these words, it is important to repeat the sentence without the qualifier, and state it with confidence.

Your ability to speak confidently and assertively affects how others view you. It sends a direct message to your spouse that you have regained your confidence and that you are in charge of your life. It allows you to take back your life. It is imperative that you speak with authority. Since words shape attitudes, then choose to use words that empower your belief in yourself and increase your confidence. You'll discover amazing results!

Using Your Head, Heart, and Gut

THREE OPERATING SYSTEMS TO STRENGTHEN YOUR DECISION MAKING

Once again, you already have everything you need to make the right decision. You may not believe it, but you do!

Partners frequently report that they are unsure how to handle certain situations in which they have no control. For example, a woman might explain that her husband is not participating in check-ins with her and she doesn't know how to motivate him to make them a priority. Another woman might complain about her spouse who does nothing to acknowledge her pain and it makes her feel disrespected and invisible.

We believe that every woman possesses the ability to tap into her energy and know exactly what to do; however, she may feel powerless and that interferes with her knowing. The problem is that she doesn't believe she knows what to do and, therefore, she lacks the confidence to make better decisions. She doesn't know that all the answers lie inside of her.

The formula for making healthy decisions is simple and guaranteed to be effective. It is a surefire method to access that "knowing." Every woman is incredibly astute in assessing situations. Perhaps it is her genetics from when the earth's earliest women oversaw everyone's safety while the men were away hunting for food. She had to know how to manage the home, predict the children's next moves, watch for the incoming blizzard and fend off to all the wild animals that could threaten the family's safety. She learned all these skills, but as usual, they felt so natural that she did not give herself credit for knowing them.

Fast forward thousands of years. Having been a partner means that you have really had to access your operating system and, although you have been in a trauma state and have operated out of fear since discovery, you are now ready to take back your ability to make decisions which helps you to take back your life. You are heading into the restoration phase of partner betrayal and you no longer want to be defined as a partner!

To do this consider the following:

The present-day woman has three operating mechanisms tucked inside of her that she can access at any time to get the answers. Once she learns the formula, she stops repeating destructive behaviors and starts navigating through life with more confidence.

The formula is simple, and you probably use one of the components when assessing what to do in a situation. The problem is that you likely are not using the entire process to make the best decisions. We would ask you the following question to ascertain what comes most naturally to you: As you think of your own life, would you say you operate from your head (intellectually), from your heart (emotionally) or from your gut (intuitively)?

Women who make the best decisions typically operate from all three. Your mind, emotions and intuition should all be working together to formulate a reality-based plan that is user-friendly.

PREDOMINANTLY USING YOUR HEAD

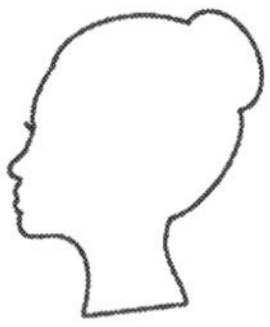

Perhaps you are the type of woman who operates from her head and relates to others in an intellectual way. Intellects know who they are. Intellectually, they can reason what is happening to them, but they are disconnected from the negative outcomes that are emotionally occurring. They can be detached from their intuition and consequently missing some important elements that help them to complete the puzzle to insure a perfect fit. It affects their ability to commit because they haven't developed a comfortable relationship with their emotions. It's like the old saying, "You can't give what you don't have." Meaning, if you aren't comfortable with your emotions, you can't share them with someone else.

Women who are predominantly "intellectualizers," primarily use thinking in their decision-making choices that are devoid of emotions or their intuition. As you might imagine, their relationships lack passion or emotion because these women "overthink" things. In addition, they are smart enough to know that something is missing in their lives and they just can't seem to identify what that is.

OPERATING PRIMARILY FROM YOUR HEART

Partners who operate solely from their emotions will continue to let their feelings direct the course. When it comes to addictive relationships, you must pay attention to what is happening around you so that you stay safe. It is important to evaluate how he is doing in recovery, so that you can assess how you will take care of yourself.

Partners who operate from their emotions are the most likely to have difficulty sorting out the complexities of loving someone who has an addiction. Emotions are not reliable navigators in looking at a situation objectively. If you make decisions solely based on your feelings, you will continue to be repeatedly wounded.

It may have been been a long time since you have experienced healthy love. Your hope was that together you would have mutually developed goals and you would have shared values that contribute to the relationship. If you allow your emotions to rule your course, you might find yourself fully loving the other person but not really loving yourself. Women who solely operate from their hearts often have difficulty making decisions regarding boundaries and consequences because they routinely change them based on their emotions. They possess "good gut," but they don't listen to that nagging feeling they get about the addict's behavior. Their intellect may also be developed, but they quickly dismiss it and let their heart do the directing. Partners who use their emotions as the primary decision maker are oftentimes flooded with emotions that interfere with good decision making.

USING YOUR GUT TO DEAL WITH THE AFTERMATH OF SEXUAL ADDICTION

Every woman has been given the gift of intuition, but she may not have been trained to pay attention to what her gut is telling her. Intuition is that "feeling or knowing" about someone or something. When sex addiction occurred and you discovered his infidelity, you likely blamed yourself for "not knowing" however you could not have known because he spent his entire existence hiding his addiction. There was nothing wrong with you or your intuition. He was a professional at deceiving you! Now that you know about his deceptions, you can count on your intuition to be your guide.

Historically, we believe that mothers have an innately well-developed sense of intuition—critical for the survival of their young. Partners who listen to their intuition once they have discovered sexual acting out have discernment skills that will help them navigate the collateral damage.

Some of you may say that you don't have that skill. Most likely you do have it, but you haven't yet recognized it or honored it. Intuition is a wonderful tool to operate from. However, most people have not been encouraged to listen to it or develop it. Intuition is really the ability to assess a situation and "know what to do about it." When women make relationship decisions based on their intuition, they are guaranteed to make healthier choices.

This skill can be enhanced by paying special attention to signs that are intuitive. Some women say they have an intuitive knowing when they feel a feeling, hear their higher power telling them what to do, when something tugs at their heartstrings or when the answer just comes to them. Those are all examples of using one's intuition. Others say that once they quiet their environment and their thoughts and focus, they hear the answer or the guidance they need.

The key to developing your intuition is to get quiet and wait for the response. It is a type of meditative process in which you become connected to the knowing inside of you. It is a spiritual process to find such a deep connection within yourself. There are many books on the intuitive process and as a therapist and coach, we recommend to women that they learn more about the gift so they can access it more readily. It is also important to learn about it so that they might pass it on to their daughters (and sons). Think about it: How often do you ask your daughter to search inside of herself to find the answer?

There are some women who have trained themselves to use all three of these powerful internal tools; their head, their heart and their gut, however, many women gravitate to only using one. If you want to make smarter decisions, have healthier relationships, and deal more positively with the world, you should work on developing each one of these gifts. As you begin, know that it will take some practice to be cognizant and to use all three of your tools.

Take some time right now and contemplate which skill you use the most. Are your decisions intellectually based or heart-driven, or do you operate from a gut feeling? Now, decide which skill you use least.

Do you reject your own thoughts and reasoning abilities? Are you afraid to trust your emotions? Do you ignore your gut feelings? The skill that you use the least is the one that will require the most development.

USING THE HEAD, HEART, AND GUT FORMULA

Write out a situation or problem that has consistently occurred in your life. You can choose a situation that specifically relates to sexual addiction or something that a woman might face in everyday life.

____

____

____

Break the problem down and ask yourself the following:

What do I think about this problem and what do I need to do about it as I reason it out?

____

____

____

How do I feel about this situation and what do my emotions drive me to do?

____

____

____

After getting quiet and thinking about the situation, what does my intuition/gut tell me to do? What do I know to do?

____

____

____

After you have written about the situation and you have written your responses, you will notice that two of the gifts support each other.

Whenever there is agreement from two of the tools, it is an automatic direction for how you need to handle the situation.

Let's look at a common problem that a woman was facing and watch how she applied the "Head, Heart, and Gut" formula to get more clarity in her life.

Amy discovered her husband's sex addiction approximately three and half years ago. She spent the first year trying to determine what had happened to her. She was in a fog. She was not thinking clearly. She was not able to communicate and sometimes the words did not come out at all. As you can imagine, she didn't trust her decisions and so she could not trust herself. Once she was in the second year of post-discovery, her brain began to heal from the trauma and she wanted to set some healthy boundaries so that she would have enough space to make healthier decisions.

Her husband was not able to stay in good recovery so she could not count on having a normal life with him in her life. She needed some real time to determine how she would proceed and keep her kids and herself in a healthy place. Normally she would have used her intellect—her head—to figure out how to proceed but her executive functioning really was out of commission for the first year due to the trauma stress response. Now that she was feeling better, her head told her she needed some distance to really think about whether she was willing to live with an addict who was not practicing good recovery. She was extremely compassionate so when he begged her forgiveness each time he slipped, she emotionally wanted to give him one more chance. Yet, intuitively she knew he was not going to stop until he hit rock bottom and she did not want to watch him go down the rabbit hole.

In many ways, her head was recommending a therapeutic separation and her gut was telling her that he might never find abstinence. When she found the time to listen to her wisdom, she knew what she needed to do. Within a month she called her support network of family and friends and she moved out. Unfortunately, his addiction worsened, and he was arrested for visiting a prostitute. He lost his job and has struggled with his ongoing addiction. Amy is thankful that she did not have to witness his demise first-hand.

Sandra was a thirty-nine-year-old, attractive, bright female who had been married twice before and had a history of unsuccessful relationships with men her whole life. She was a well-educated woman who appeared to have everything going for her, but she did not seem able to find a man who could be faithful and love her for who she was. She seemingly had everything going for her except in her ability to "find lasting love." She desperately wanted a relationship and had difficulty finding anyone who would date her longer than three months.

As she searched for patterns in her interaction with men, it became apparent that when she started dating a man, she would inundate him with expectations. As soon as the end of the first week and sometimes even the first date, she would start assessing whether he was marriage material. She would begin to expect daily phone calls and frequent dates. She would have sex with him within the first two dates and then assume that she had the commitment she so desperately needed. She would quickly tell him that she expected to hear from him by Wednesday if they were to go out by

Friday, and then she would act disgruntled if he did not meet her deadlines. Her over-dependence ended up pushing each man away. Because he had not really established a solid connection with her, he would typically try to fade out of the picture, which would then result in a rant about the double messages he had sent to her.

Since she was able to cite at least twelve relationships that ended up disappointing her, she was willing to assess things using the Head, Heart, and Gut formula.

Here was the work that she did:

- **Intellectual**—What Does She Think When She Uses Her Head?

  "When I think through things intellectually, I realize that I am moving faster in the relationship than the men I date. I don't give them enough time to plan the dates or call me. I know that men need to feel like they are in control, and I know that I tend to want to teach them how to date."

- **Emotionally:** How Does She Feel When She Uses Her Heart?

  "I am tired of being alone and I want someone to love me. When I get into relationships, I want to be pursued and so I shower them with affection hoping to get that in return. But the more I give, the more they take. What I want most in my life is to be loved and cared for."

- **Intuition:** What Does Her Intuition and Gut Tell Her About the Situation?

  "My gut tells me to slow down and let the guy make the plans. Even before I start to text, I wonder if I should let him text me first, but I just can't stop myself, so I initiate contact. I don't want to listen to or trust my gut!

  "All my friends tell me to stop fantasizing about what could be and to stay in the moment. I am afraid that if I don't stay on top of things, I will be ignored or forgotten, so I move it along a bit. My gut tells me to have faith that I will find the right guy or that God will take care of this, but I would rather do it myself."

In Sandra's scenario her head was telling her to slow down, her heart was telling her to give unconditionally so that she would find someone who would love her, and her gut was telling her to have faith that things would turn out if she stopped working at it so hard.

You can clearly see that in this scenario, Sandra's "need to be loved" was sabotaging the very thing that she wanted. Her emotions were clearly driving her actions and getting in the way of her desired outcome. When she could see with clarity what was happening, she was able to understand that her work would entail using more of her head and her gut energy while she practiced dating. This would invariably result in the outcome she wanted. She needed to start practicing using her intellect and her intuition to create the life she deserved. It took fourteen months, but once Sandra learned to use her head and her gut in combination with her heart, she was able to meet a man who loved her unconditionally and with whom she could depend on with certainty.

This simple formula is another tool that you can add to your tool belt, because when things aren't working, it makes sense to try something that does. And what better tools to use but the special gifts you have been given—like your head, your heart, and your gut!

KNOWING YOUR PERSONALITY STRENGTHS

One of the greatest gifts you can give yourself is to recognize your own self-worth. When you started this workbook you likely felt that you lacked self-confidence. Initially the visualization and other empowering techniques were difficult because "deep down inside" when the betrayal occurred it left you not feeling good enough. The crisis stole your sense of confidence and left you lacking a belief in yourself. But you learned that your self-esteem was not dependent on his addiction nor the wounds that came from it. You have worked hard and you own your work.

Part of the healing process requires a recognition of your own self-worth. Being in posttraumatic growth means that you own your strengths!

Would you be able to write down 50 of your own strengths? What strengths do you admire about yourself? Although this is a challenging exercise, it is also a reminder that your brilliance as a person is within you, and that you are the person who takes it for granted. Good self-esteem requires knowing and appreciating your attributes. You may have been taught to be humble, but acknowledging your strengths allows you to better create the life you deserve.

If you were to do the personality strength exercise, would you naturally minimize your strengths? At the beginning of your work in this journal did you invalidate your uniqueness and your gifts? Would you have qualified your words with self-doubt? If you wrote self-assured, would you automatically challenge yourself because you feel intimidated every time you go to a restaurant with your husband? Initially would you have compared yourself to every woman in the room and wonder if he was fantasizing about her? Now you know that if he is not working his tools, that is for him to reckon with and it has nothing to do with you!

Even in posttraumatic growth, it's not unusual to want to question your positive opinions of yourself after sexual betrayal, yet the exercise is meant to highlight your strengths and renew your sense of confidence separate from him.

Coming up with 50 positive adjectives to describe yourself may require focus. If you are having trouble, ask ten people to identify what they admire most about you. Many people resist asking others because they fear that others could not identify any admirable qualities.

True self-confidence requires a certain comfort level with your attributes and your insecurities. Getting feedback from others will reinforce what you subconsciously know about yourself but have lost your ability to feel.

Retraining your brain takes effort and you have worked hard to break the cycle of partner betrayal. Knowing and owning your strengths changes who you are and sets you up for lots of great things in your life. It can be helpful for you to process this information by writing them down somewhere so that it can be easily accessed when you need an extra boost of self-confidence. This is empowering because it reinforces your strengths. As a result, you will be less likely to question yourself in the face of your own self-criticism. Again, this is another sign of posttraumatic growth!

PERSONALITY STRENGTHS CHALLENGE

When you started this process you were likely too tough on yourself and placed too high of expectations on yourself which was unachievable. This exercise is to assist you in identifying your personality strengths that strengthen your posttraumatic growth and make you powerful beyond measure.

OBJECTIVE

This exercise will fortify your special qualities that you had prior to partner betrayal and it will promote resiliency, empowerment and good self-esteem. It will remind you of how far you have come in your journey. It will reinforce that his addiction had nothing to do with how you looked, how you behaved or what personality strengths you possessed prior to the discovery of his sexual addiction.

Complete the following assignment

1. Find a quiet spot and center yourself for 3 minutes.

2. Write down 50 adjectives/words that describe your personality.

The words must be positive. Remember to use personality strengths only. If you think "I am a good mother," ask yourself what adjectives make up being a good mother and include the adjectives in the list. You may list "nurturing," "protective" or "loving."

Note: It is common for negative thoughts to come up as one thinks of positive words. Ignore the inner critic and write only positive words as part of your list.

Remember that this is not a time to be humble. This is an opportunity to name and reclaim your strengths prior to sexual betrayal! You are reinforcing all the changes you have made! Keep this list close so that you can remind yourself of your incredible qualities.

Good self-esteem is the foundation that has enabled you to get through this crisis. There is a coaching formula that frequently reminds partners how to stay steadfast in their confidence:

Be ~ Do ~ Have

You must **be**, which involves being connected to the power within yourself. You must **do** the work to move beyond the partner betrayal which will insure that you **have** a stronger sense of self and empowerment.

Strengths

1.	26.
2.	27.
3.	28.
4.	29.
5.	30.
6.	31.
7.	32.
8.	33.
9.	34.
10.	35.
11.	36.
12.	37.
13.	38.
14.	39.
15.	40.
16.	41.
17.	42.
18.	43.
19.	44.
20.	45.
21.	46.
22.	47.
23.	48.
24.	49.
25.	50.

CHAPTER 10

You Have Changed

NOW IT IS TIME TO FIND YOUR PURPOSE!

You Have Entered Into Posttraumatic Growth

This workbook was designed to help you work through the trauma and refocus on you. Once you have assessed what you need to feel happiness, you will be much more likely to have the desire to actualize your potential.

His addiction has changed you, but you made the decision to use the trauma to get stronger and healthier. You are no longer defined by betrayal trauma. You have become resilient! Now that you have regained your sanity, you may be looking for ways to give back or help others to change. You may want to help other partners that are struggling with the discovery that their spouse has an addiction. You might decide to volunteer at your child's school to have more involvement in your child's environment. You may decide to write a memoir to help other women who are going through partner betrayal.

Once you enter into posttraumatic growth, you will recognize your changes and you will feel so grateful that "your spirit is back" and that you have a renewed sense of energy to contribute to the world. You may actually have felt a nudge to create more meaning in your life.

Have you felt something tugging at your heartstrings to actualize or pursue?

When things get quiet and the distractions are few, is there a nagging feeling that continues to haunt you, reminding you that there is a calling inside of you that you may be choosing to ignore perhaps because of time constraints or the need to stay steadfast in your course of recovery? We are glad that you are pacing yourself and not taking on too much, but if and when you decide to move towards finding your purpose, we are wholeheartedly behind you!

When the time is right, you will know that it is time to pursue that vision. You only live once, so it is absolutely your responsibility to make the most of your life. This life is not a dress rehearsal. "Go for the gusto" and act on your intuition and your knowing that you have more to do in your life. If you believe that you may be held back by a lack of confidence or insecurity, face your vulnerability and push through it! If you believe that fear may be slowing you down, move beyond the fears that may keep you a bystander in your own life and do it anyway!

You have been through a lot but see yourself as having gotten to the other side of this crisis with accrued strength and wisdom. This requires that you make a concerted effort to "stretch" or "move out of your comfort zone." Inevitably, when you choose to stretch, you are making a choice to do something different. This will give you a taste of something new and lead you through a growth experience. It will add to your repertoire of life experiences and it increases your life skills. We tell women they don't need to be successful. Their success comes not from the outcome but from moving from one comfort zone to the next level, which usually involves taking risks, practicing different skills and stretching out of your comfort zone enough to feel fear. Brené Brown calls this "Daring Greatly" and quotes Theodore Roosevelt as saying "The credit belongs to the man who is actually in the arena...who spends himself in a worthy cause. Who at the best knows in the end the triumph of high achievement and who at the worse if he fails, at least fails while daring greatly..." In other words, it's not the outcome; it's the effort a person makes to do something different that creates sustained change and truly makes a difference.

Having said that, we also believe it's imperative that you have a game plan to get you where you are going. If you consistently feel that little gnawing reminder that you need to be doing something new, you must plan for that.

Is there something in your life that you would love to pursue, but you either don't know how to make it happen or your fear keeps you from doing it?

Live Your Life to the Fullest

We believe that you were born for greatness and that you have heard "that quiet whisper" that has encouraged you to pursue your passion and actualize your dreams.

What has been tugging at your heartstrings? When you write it down, you are more likely to make it happen.

We have worked with thousands of women who, during their treatment or coaching, have identified things they have always wanted to do.

Surround yourself with encouraging statements that will remind you of your brilliance. We recommend that you purchase the Marianne Williamson quote from Return to Love and place it somewhere where you will see it several times a day to remind you of your ongoing resilience.

Conclusion

Working through partner betrayal has required great strength and immense courage. You have walked through the process and your job is to continue to work from the third phase of healing known as restoration. You have likely been able to see that posttraumatic stress has also contributed to posttraumatic growth, which means that this process has strengthened your sense of self and what you will accept in life.

Now that you have finished this workbook, we trust that you are able to see your progress and acknowledge it. We know that you are a much different woman now that you have invested in yourself and done the work needed to heal from the infidelity.

We applaud the time you have spent improving your skills and know that you will be much more likely to get your needs met because of all your hard work.

Our mission is to improve the lives of partners by raising awareness and teaching the skills necessary to change lives. If you wished that you could have shared this work with another woman who needed to strengthen their sense of self, we are pleased to tell you that we have created another version for women who want the opportunity to grow but may not have experienced the betrayal and trauma that you faced. That book is called *Transformations: A Woman's Journey of Self-Discovery* and it uses many of the same exercises for self-growth without the trauma catalyst that you have been through because of the partner betrayal.

We know that all women need support in moving through their lives. Thank you for allowing us to be part of your healing.

May your journey be blessed as you also improve the lives of the people you impact...especially your daughters, mothers, and girlfriends!

Carol & Christine

Bibliography

Adams, Kenneth M. *Silently Seduced: When Parents Make Their Children Partners.* Rev. & updated ed. Deerfield Beach, FL: Health Communications, 2011.

Amen, Daniel G. *Change Your Brain, Change Your Life: The Breakthrough Program for Conquering Anxiety, Depression, Obsessiveness, Lack of Focus, Anger, and Memory Problems.* 2nd ed. New York: Harmony Books, 2015.

Carnes, Patrick J. *The Betrayal Bond: Breaking Free of Exploitive Relationships.* Deerfield Beach, FL: Health Communications, 1999.

---. *Out of the Shadows: Understanding Sexual Addiction.* Center City, MN: Hazelden Publishing, 2001.

Carnes, Stephanie et al. *Facing Heartbreak: Steps to Recovery for Partners of Sex Addicts.* Carefree, AZ: Gentle Path Press, 2012.

Carnes, Stefanie. *Mending a Shattered Heart: A Guide for Partners of Sex Addicts.* 2nd ed. Carefree, AZ: Gentle Path Press, 2011.

---. Courageous Love: *A Couples Guide to Conquering Betrayal*, Carefree, AZ: Gentle Path Press, 2020.

Caudill, Janice, and Dan Drake. *Full Disclosure: Preparing Partners for Full Disclosure.* Kintsugi Recovery Partners, 2019.

---. *Full Disclosure: Seeking Truth After Sexual Betrayal, Volume I for Partners: How Disclosure Can Help You Heal*

---. *Full Disclosure: Seeking Truth After Sexual Betrayal, Volume II for Partners: Preparing for Disclosure on Your Terms*

Cloud, Henry, and John Townsend. *Boundaries: When to Say Yes, How to Say No to Take Control of Your Life.* Grand Rapids: Zondervan, 1992.

---. *Boundaries in Marriage.* Grand Rapids: Zondervan, 2002.

---. *How People Grow: What the Bible Reveals about Personal Growth.* Grand Rapids: Zondervan, 2001.

---. *Safe People: How to Find Relationships that Are Good for You and Avoid Those that Aren't.* Grand Rapids: Zondervan, 2016.

Corley, M. Deborah, and Jennifer P. Schneider. *Disclosing Secrets: An Addict's Guide for When, to Whom, and How Much to Reveal.* Tucson, AZ: Recovery Resources Press, 2012.

Courtois, Christine A. *It's Not You, It's What Happened to You: Complex Trauma and Treatment.* Self-published: Telemachus Press, 2014.

Denison, Beth. *12-Week Partner Recovery Guide Journey to Healing from Sexual Betrayal.* Fortworth, Tx: Austin Brothers Publishing, 2020.

Hall, Laurie. *An Affair of the Mind.* Colorado Springs: Focus on the Family, 1996.

Keffer, Sheri. *Intimate Deception: Healing the Wounds of Sexual Betrayal.* Grand Rapids Revell. Baker Publishing Group, 2018.

Magness, Milton S. *Stop Sex Addiction: Real Hope, True Freedom for Sex Addicts and Partners.* Las Vegas, NV: Central Recovery Press, 2013.

Porges, Stephen W. *The Polyvagal Theory: Neurophysiological Foundations of Emotions, Attachment, Communication, and Self-Regulation.* New York: W.W. Norton, 2011.

Sheets, Carol J., and Allan J. Katz. *Help. Her. Heal.: An Empathy Workbook for Sex Addicts to Help Their Partners Heal.* Sano Press, 2019.

Sheets, Carol J., and Christine Turo-Shields. *Transformations: A Woman's Journey of Self-Discovery* Sano Press, 2020.

Steffens, Barbara A., and Marsha Means. *Your Sexually Addicted Spouse: How Partners Can Cope and Heal.* Far Hills, NJ: New Horizon Press, 2009.

Van der Kolk, Bessel A. *The Body Keeps the Score: Brain, Mind and Body in the Healing of Trauma.* New York: Viking, 2014.

Weiss, Douglas. *Married and Alone: Practical Exercises for Healing.* Colorado Springs: Discovery Press, 2011.

Resources

PARTNER SENSITIVE TRAINING ORGANIZATIONS

- *The Association of Partners of Sex Addicts Trauma Specialists* APSATS.org. They have a Directory to find Partner Sensitive Clinicians or Coaches

- *The International Institute for Trauma and Addiction Professionals* IITAP.org. They have a Directory to find Certified Sexual Addiction Therapists and Partner Specialists

- *The Association of Traumatic Stress Specialist ATSS.* They are an international organization dedicated to excellence in services and support to individuals impacted by trauma.

TRAUMA HOTLINE

- *Posttraumatic Stress Disorder Hotline*: 1 (800) 273-TALK

ONLINE COURSES FOR PARTNER SENSITIVE HEALING

- www.sexhelpwithcarolthecoach/HelpHerHeal
  Online Empathy Course for Sex Addicts to Help Their Partners Heal

- www.sexhelpwithcarolthecoach/PartnersFindYourPostTraumaticGrowth
  Online Posttraumatic Growth Course to Move Partners Beyond Betrayal

- www.affairrecovery.com Harboring Hope: Online Course for Betrayed Spouses.

PARTNER SENSITIVE WEBSITES, THERAPISTS AND COACHES

- Carol Juergensen Sheets AKA Carol the Coach
  - https://www.sexhelpwithcarolthecoach.com
  - https://www.carolthecoach.com

- Christine Turo-Shields, LCSW, EMDR certified
    - http://www.kenosiscenter.com
- Marnie Breecker.
    - http://www.helpingcouplesheal.com
- Lyschel Burkett. Hope Redefined offers faith based online support groups, coaching, for women facing sexual betrayal
    - http://www.HopeRedefined.org
- Jodi F. Conway
    - https://www.newenglandrecoveryassociates.com/
    - https://www.newenglandrecoveryassociates.com/betrayed-partners-groups-sex-addiction-boston-new-england-recovery-associates#MENSSEXADDICTIONGROUPFORBUILDINGEMPATHYSKILLS
- Beth Denison
    - https://www.theresstillhope.org/hope-for-the-spouse
- Donna Meredith Dixon. ADOH Peer Facilitator Training
    - https://www.lifeisahead.com/
- Gaelyn Rae Emerson
    - https://www.womeneverafter.com
      Specialized support for betrayal-related grief, betrayal-related divorce and self-rediscovery in the aftermath of relational trauma.
- Debee Ferree
    - coachdebbieferree@gmail.com
- Local and Online Support Partner Groups/Face to Face Coaching
    - https://www.SalHarper.com

- Leanna Harvey
    - https://www.lighthouse-counseling.com
- Susan Hastie. Online Groups for Female Partners
    - https://szhastie.wixsite.com/susan-hastie
- Rebecca Hogg
    - www.canvascw.com (Concierge Therapy Services)
- Fran Hopwood and Richard Butler. Help for Partners, Couples and SAs
    - www.holding-hope.com
- Grace Ventures, LLC Counseling and Coaching Services
    - www.gvcounsel.com gvcounsel@gmail.com
- Rebecca Maestas, LCSW, CCPS. Christian Counseling & Coaching
    - www.becomingyou.coach
- Shawna Meek, CPC, PCC, CPC. Betrayal Trauma Support Group for Women
    - www.livingstonescoaching.com
- Partner Support Group – Michigan / Telehealth
    - www.northpoint-counseling.com
- The Naked Truth Project in the UK
    - https://www.nakedtruthrecovery.com/wholehearted
- Kirsi Paulin. Partner sensitive work in Europe, Finland
    - www.tnnky.fi/salvia
- Kim Petroni
    - https://www.coachinghope4u.com

- Jenni Rochelle, Betrayal Trauma Specialist
    - www.jennirochelle.com
- Two Hearts Coaching, Online Support Groups for Partners
    - www.twoheartscoaching.com
- Karen Rellos
    - www.Redeeming-love.com
    - karenrellos@gmail.com

PODCASTS

- Carol the Coach
    - https://blogtalkradio.com/sexhelpwithcarolthecoach.com
- Carol the Coach for APSATS.org
    - https://blogtalkradio.com/betrayalrecoveryradio.com
- Race and Recovery for Women of Color. Andrea Rogers.
    - https://podcasts.apple.com/us/podcast/betrayal-recovery-radio/id1396715281?i=1000475345238
- Therapy Extended with Liza Young
    - https://www.lizayoungcounseling.com/podcast

BLOGS

- www.Pornandsexaddiction.net One Couples Journey
- Carol the Coach
    - https://www.sexhelpwithcarolthecoach.com
    - https://www.carolthecoach.com

INTENSIVES

- Support for Partners whose Spouses are in the Begin Again Institute
    - https://www.beginagaininstitute.com/product/partners
      Begin Again Partner Support Program.

      Every day of the intensive, partners receive an encouraging email with educational resources to help them navigate betrayal trauma. Partners also receive 10 hours of group coaching with other partners whose loved ones are at the same BAI intensive. There is a private Facebook group where partners meet 24/7 and support each other.
- Intensives for Couples, Betrayed Partners, and Actors
  CORE Relationship Recovery
  www.HopeForUs.com
- Dr. Crystal Hollenbeck
    - Three Day Trauma Healing Intensives
    - www.CrystalHollenbeck.com

RETREATS

Hope Redefined offers faith based intensive healing for women facing sexual betrayal.

- www.HopeRedefined.org

YOUTUBE VIDEOS FOR PARTNERS AND ADDICTS

- Sex Help with Carol the Coach for Sex Addiction/Partner Betrayal/Coupleship
- Carol the Coach for Goal Setting
- Carol Juergensen Sheets for Actualizing Your Potential

About Carol

Carol Juergensen Sheets, ACSW, LCSW, CSAT, CCPS-C, PCC is a highly regarded social worker, personal life coach and a renowned self-help author who brings a variety of experiences to her clients and readers including having worked in schools, hospitals and in mental health for over 40 years. She has worked for 4 decades facilitating thousands of groups for women and teens. Additionally, Carol has devoted the last 2 decades to helping men and women manage their sex addiction and helping betrayed partners work through the trauma of sexual and relational betrayal. She is a much-loved sex and relationship therapist to individuals and couples across the country and beyond.

Carol completed her master's degree at the honorable institution, Indiana University School of Social Work. She is currently facilitating popular workshops on relationships both statewide and nationally. Carol does annual workshops for the International Institute for Trauma and Addiction Professionals. She is also a revered trainer for the Association of Partners of Sex Addicts Trauma Specialists and is a consultant for clinicians and coaches for APSATS.

Carol very much enjoys facilitating group and couples work and has facilitated thousands of groups in the last 3 decades. She has been a highly sought-after executive and life coach for over 15 years and loves motivating her clients to reach their greatest potential.

Carol's breakout book *Help. Her. Heal.* has been sold in countries around the world including Canada, Denmark, Japan, England, France and Australia. Primarily written for male partners of wives, fiancées and girlfriends (yet also extremely helpful for females and couples), *Help. Her. Heal.* deals with assisting men with problematic sexual behavior to develop their relational skills to help their partners heal through the powerful use of empathy.

Help. Her. Heal. explores the necessity for the sex addict to work on both his individual recovery needs and his relational skills. So that addicts will be able to navigate through the devastation caused by sexual addiction, Carol teaches her all-important signature formula AVR, which is Acknowledging the issue, Validating the primary feeling, and then Reassuring the betrayed partner of the changes that are being made.

The book beautifully addresses how men can access and develop empathy for their female partners, particularly checking in with their partner's fears and needs and practicing healthy behaviors and practices. The book aids men in how to deal with conflict after betrayal, as well as techniques to stay strong while they help their partners heal. Finally, *Help. Her. Heal.* deftly addresses the complex rituals of connection, trust and restoration that can heal a broken relationship.

Carol believes in teaching people how to live their best lives in romance and in life in general. She has hosted radio shows and podcasts over her entire professional career. Also known as "Carol the Coach", Carol hosts www.blogtalkradio.com/sexhelpwithcarolthecoach to help her listeners understand the complexities of sexual addiction and partner betrayal. She also hosts a podcast specifically for partners to navigate through the trauma of sexual betrayal called, www.blogtalkradio.com/betrayalrecoveryradio for APSATS.org.

Carol also hosts highly productive teleseminars that feature goal setting, relationship building and shortcuts to positive self-esteem.

Carol has written columns in newspapers and magazines to help people grow emotionally and enhance their well-being. You can read over 500 articles on her website www.carolthecoach.com or go to her sex addiction website for sex addicts or partners at: www.sexhelpwithcarolthecoach.com

When asked about her profession, Carol says: "I have been blessed to help people all over the world! My work has been a platform for psychotherapy, speaking engagements, radio and television, newspaper and magazine articles and now the books that are helping men and women heal. Early on in my life I learned that my passion was to help people navigate through the trauma of their childhood and adult life and to move them into posttraumatic growth where they would develop resiliency and actualize their potential."

Carol Juergensen Sheets is a best-selling author for the esteemed publishing company Sano Press.

Carol Juergensen Sheets ACSW, LCSW, CSAT, CCPS-C, PCC

EMDR Certified Therapist

Strategic Coaching and Therapies

3815 River Crossing Pkwy, Suite 100 Indianapolis, IN 46240

(317) 847-2244 | carol@carolthecoach.com

About Christine

Christine Turo-Shields, ACSW, LCSW, LCAC brings hope and humor, energy and enthusiasm to her work with children, families and adults. For over 30 years, she has provided therapy in a variety of settings, including individual, marital, family and group counseling. Her expertise is rich with various clinical passion areas, including women's empowerment, anxiety/panic disorders, depression, abuse/trauma/PTSD, addictions as well as with those who are gifted/profoundly gifted. Blending CBT with mindfulness and hope for the future, Christine brings people to a place of recovery and restoration, whatever their struggle may be, including an exploration of aspects of faith and spirituality amidst their journey of life.

Christine completed her master's degree at Indiana University School of Social Work where the values of empowerment and self-care were deeply imprinted upon her. She is statewide and national workshop presenter on a variety of clinical topics including women's issues, posttraumatic growth, trauma and survivor loss recovery, faith and spirituality, anxiety management as well as the blessings and burdens of the gifted and their families.

She is an avid believer in the power of healing through groups and has facilitated thousands of women's and teen groups with Carol Juergensen Sheets over the last 3 decades. She currently facilitates a group for gifted women who struggle with anxiety and depression as well as an emotion regulation/anxiety management group. She was extremely blessed and honored to facilitate a posttraumatic growth group for those who had experienced the loss of a loved one from a traumatic death—it was one of the most profound and humbling experiences of her professional career.

Christine is certified in EMDR Therapy (Eye Movement Desensitization and Reprocessing), which is a highly effective treatment for trauma. As an Indiana State Board Member of the American Foundation for Suicide Prevention (AFSP), she works extensively with survivors of suicide loss, including providing suicide prevention trainings at local churches, schools and interested organizations. She also has clinical specialty with women suffer with perinatal mood disorders, and she has been a guest presenter for Postpartum Support International (PSI) Indianapolis training regarding the effectiveness of EMDR for those who have experienced birth trauma or have had a history of sexual abuse.

Additionally, she is a nationally trained provider for the National Center for Missing & Exploited Children and is a member of NCMEC's Family Advocacy Outreach Network, providing therapeutic services and support to local families with missing and exploited children to address family trauma, reunification and adjustment.

As a co-owner of Kenosis Counseling Center, Inc., a community-based private practice, she provides clinical supervision to graduate interns as well as professionals who are working towards licensure. Guiding them as they develop clinical skills, she encourages professional caregivers to also make self-care a priority, become more mindful, and practice balance in order that they thrive rather than exist. She has received training through Vanderbilt's Distressed Physicians Program and has worked to support physicians as they navigate professional pressures. Christine believes that daily investment in self enhances a one's ability to tend to others' needs both personally and professionally over the long-term.

As a consummate extrovert, Christine is always open to providing trainings...to inquire, you can email her at christine@kenosiscenter.com or visit the website www.kenosiscenter.com

Christine Turo-Shields ACSW, LCSW, LCAC

EMDR Certified Therapist
Kenosis Counseling Center, Inc.
1678 Fry Road, Suite D. Greenwood, IN 46142
(317) 865-1674 | christine@kenosiscenter.com

Made in the USA
Middletown, DE
04 August 2021

45406886R00113